WORKBOOK

Student Notes and Problems

SCIENCE 10

Alberta Edition

Castle Rock
Research Corp

Canadian Cataloguing in Publication Data

Rao, Gautam, 1961 –

STUDENT NOTES AND PROBLEMS – Science 10 Workbook (AB)

1. Science – Juvenile Literature. I. Title

Published by

Castle Rock Research Corp.

2340 Manulife Place

10180 – 101 Street

Edmonton, AB T5J 3S4

8 9 10 FP 13 12 11

Printed in Canada

Publisher
Gautam Rao

Contributors
Terry Olfert
Bob Clarke
Sanjay Sharma

Dedicated to the memory of Dr. V. S. Rao

STUDENT NOTES AND PROBLEMS WORKBOOKS

Student Notes and Problems (SNAP) workbooks are a series of support resources in mathematics for students in grades 3 to 12 and in science for students in grades 9 to 12. SNAP workbooks are 100% aligned with curriculum. The resources are designed to support classroom instructions and provide students with additional examples, practice exercises, and tests. SNAP workbooks are ideal for use all year long at school and at home.

The following is a summary of the key features of all SNAP workbooks.

UNIT OPENER

- summarizes the curriculum outcomes addressed in the unit in age-appropriate language
- identifies the lessons by title
- lists the prerequisite knowledge and skills the student should know prior to beginning the unit

LESSONS

- provide essential teaching pieces and explanations of the concepts
- include example problems and questions with complete, detailed solutions that demonstrate the problem-solving process

NOTES BARS

- contain key definitions, formulas, reminders, and important steps or procedures
- provide space for students to add their own notes and helpful reminders

PRACTICE EXERCISES

- include questions that relate to each of the curriculum outcomes for the unit
- provide practice in applying the lesson concepts

REVIEW SUMMARY

- provides a succinct review of the key concepts in the unit

PRACTICE TEST

- assesses student learning of the unit concepts

ANSWERS AND SOLUTIONS

- demonstrate the step-by-step process or problem-solving method used to arrive at the correct answer

Answers and solutions are provided in each workbook for the odd-numbered questions. A SNAP *Solutions Manual* that contains answers and complete solutions for all questions is also available.

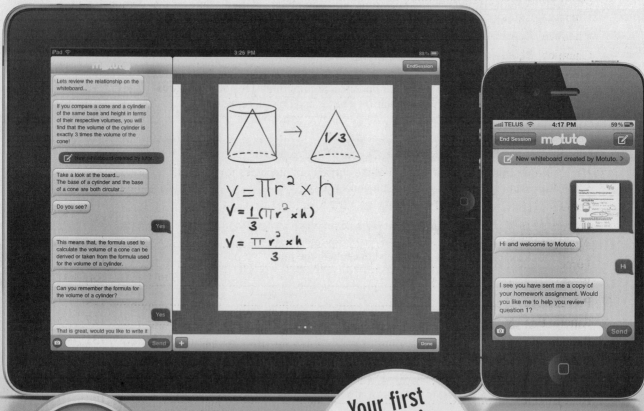

CONTENTS

Energy and Matter in Chemical Change

Energy Flow in Technological Systems

Cycling of Matter in Living Systems

Energy Flow in Global Systems

Answers and Solutions

ENERGY AND MATTER IN CHEMICAL CHANGE

When you are finished this unit, you will be able to understand...

- classification of matter based on chemical and physical properties
- elements and the Periodic Table, common life elements and the use of separation and classification techniques using technology
- atomic, ionic, and molecular shapes and sizes through the use of models
- chemical bonding and nomenclature
- organic chemistry necessary to life
- energy changes of matter in chemical reactions
- physical and chemical changes by performing experiments
- conservation of mass in chemical reactions

PREREQUISITE SKILLS AND KNOWLEDGE

Aristotle 400 BC	Democritus 400 BC	Dalton AD 1800
Fire, earth, water, and air	Believed that material was made up of small indivisible particles called "atoms"	Believed that each element is made up of indivisible particles called atoms; each element has different properties
	water salt steel	Copper Gold Oxygen
J. J. Thompson AD 1900	**Rutherford AD 1920**	**Bohr AD 1930**
Discovered that atoms had negative particles (electron) contained inside the atom	Believed that electrons were outside the dense positive part of the atom (nucleus)	Thought that electrons were arranged in certain energy levels around the positive nucleus

beryllium |
| Lithium   Hydrogen | Lithium   Helium | Beryllium |

**Quantum Mechanical Model
AD 1940**

Uses electron cloud model in which electrons are not considered to be point charges but as a mist around the nucleus

beryllium

$2e-$
$2e-$

$4+$

Beryllium

Lesson 1 MATTER

States of Matter

There are three states of matter:
- solid
- liquid
- gas

Three states of matter:
- solid
- liquid
- gas

All matter exists in one of three states. For example, H_2O can be solid (ice), liquid (water), for gas (steam).

The Kinetic Molecular Theory of Matter states that all matter is made of moving particles and that when the particles gain energy, they move faster. When moving faster, they bump into each other more often and with more force. With more energy, these particles push each other apart, causing an increase in pressure on the container they are in, or they push into a new area. Eventually, the molecules separate enough that a phase change occurs. Phase changes occur between states of matter; for example, from solid to liquid or from liquid to gas.

Phase changes:
solid $\leftrightarrow$ liquid
liquid $\leftrightarrow$ gas

When ice is heated, the crystals are forced to separate and liquid water is formed. With more heat, the water molecules continue to push each other apart, causing the liquid to vaporize into a gas: steam.

The phase change temperature of each element and molecule is unique. Every molecule or atom has a specific temperature at which it will change state. This signature boiling point and melting point can be used to identify the substance. Water melts at 0°C and vaporizes at 100°C.

Water:
melting point 0°C
boiling point 100°C

NOTES

Physical Changes

When a quantity of an element such as gold goes from solid to liquid or gas, the change is called a physical change because the physical properties of the gold change. The atom is identical, but the space between the atoms increases.

Physical properties measured in chemistry are either

- qualitative (use senses to detect these)
- quantitative (measurable using the correct instruments)

Qualitative Physical Properties

- colour
- texture
- taste
- smell
- state
- shape
- malleability (ability to be pounded into shapes)
- ductility (ability to be stretched into a wire)

Examples of Qualitative Physical Properties (at room temperature)

- helium and hydrogen are colourless gases
- chlorine is a yellowish gas
- sodium is a silvery-grey solid
- carbon is a black solid

Quantitative Physical Properties

- melting point
- boiling point
- density
- viscosity (how well the substance flows)
- solubility (how well the substance dissolves into a solvent)
- conductivity (how well the substance can conduct heat and electricity)

Examples of physical properties for three common substances are given in the following table

Physical Property	Gold	Water	Table Salt
Colour	Gold colour	Colourless	White
State at room temperature	Solid	Liquid	Solid
Malleability	Easily rolled into a sheet	Not malleable	Not malleable
Ductility	Easily stretched into wire	Not ductile	Not ductile
Melting point	1 064°C	0°C	801°C
Boiling/condensation point	2 808°C	100°C	Very high
Solubility	Will dissolve in salt water over time	Does dissolve	Does dissolve
Conductivity	Very conductive	Slightly conductive	Conductive

Chemical Changes

Chemical changes occur when compounds or elements react together to create a new compound. For example, when chlorine and sodium are combined, they produce salt (NaCl, or sodium chloride), which has different properties than either of the original chemicals.

All compounds and elements can also be classified by their chemical properties. Identification tests can be done to see if a compound or element reacts with water, air, pure oxygen, acids, and other pure substances.

- Flame test – Every substance burns with a unique coloured flame and combusts at a particular temperature.
  O_2 – blue
  Ca – red
  Cu – green
  Na – yellow
  Li – pink
  K – violet
  Ba – lime

Flame test — dip a wire into a solution containing certain elements; the flame will change colour as it burns. Each element has its own unique flame colour and flash point.

- The *flash* or *ignition point*. The flash point is the lowest temperature at which a liquid is ignitable. For example, the flash point of ethyl alcohol (C_2H_6O) is 16°C.
- The reactivity of the substance with:
  air – tarnish
  water – corrosive/dissolving
  acids – corrosive
  heat – melt and/or decompose
  acid-base indicator: litmus—red – acid, blue – base

Tests can also be conducted to see if elements and compounds are toxic, stable at room temperature, or combustible.

Coal burns readily once it is ignited, but it will not ignite spontaneously when in contact with the air. Some metals such as rubidium and cesium must be stored in oil or they will begin to burn when exposed to air.

If sodium is dropped into water, it will dance around until it vaporizes. If potassium is placed on the water's surface, it will create a small explosion. This chemical reaction is used in some bombs. When they explode, small pieces of potassium fly out and burn any organic matter composed of 70% to 90% water.

Storing food requires knowledge of both chemical properties and reactions of the chemicals used.

Heating (cooking) and freezing is used to sterilize and preserve foods. Both heating and freezing involve chemical changes.

Flame test – dip a wire into a solution containing certain elements; the flame will change color as it burns. Each element has its own unique flame colour and flash point.

Salting is used to dry meat out (salt absorbs water from the meat). Dehydrating meat prevents bacteria from living on it. Sailors made use of this storage method. The Egyptians also used this methodology as they preserved grain in very dry, dark buildings. We still have grain that has been stored for over 2 000 years that will grow if it is planted today.

Fermentation is another chemical preservative technique.
When a substance is fermented, the lactobacilli present on almost all foods convert starch to sugars, which preserves the food. One can still purchase old foods and wines made hundreds of years ago if they were fermented and stored correctly.

Smoking foods also prevents spoiling, as wood smoke increases the antioxidant and formaldehyde concentrations.

Metallurgy

Around 3000 BC, the production of metals was limited to what was found at hand. When people acquired an understanding of how to use heat, gold and copper were purified. These were then made into jewelry and tools. The annealing (or heating) of copper before it is hammered into a shape set the pattern for future metal work. Smelting is the purifying of a metal by using heat. Melting copper separates out the impurities. The Egyptians smelted the element copper over 4 000 years ago.

Whether by accident or intent, the Sumerians (2500 BC) mixed molten tin and copper. This alloy had new characteristics of strength but increased the weight of the substance. This discovery began the Bronze Age, which lasted until 100 BC when iron and carbon were combined to form steel another alloy, which has become the most produced alloy the world has known.

Brass Alloy
• 60% copper
• 39% zinc
• 1% tin

PRACTICE EXERCISE

1. Indicate whether the following reactions are physical or chemical.

Reaction	Physical	Chemical
Melting ice		
Burning paper		
Making dry ice (solidification of carbon dioxide)		
Cooking a hamburger		
Boiling water		
Burning natural gas in a furnace		
Making wine by fermentation		
Boiling an egg		

2. Give the name of the person who first proposed the following idea or the name of the theory that contains the idea.

Example	Person / Theory
Pure elements are made up of atoms	
Fire is a type of matter	
Electrons are in a cloud surrounding nuclear particles	
Salt is an atom	
Electrons occupy certain energy levels	

3. State four physical properties of gold.

    •

    •

    •

    •

4. Which of the following properties is a chemical property?

    A) Melts at 200°C   **B)** Conducts an electric current
    C) Turns red litmus blue   **D)** Solid at room temperature

5. Which of the following substances is an example of an alloy?

   A) Dry ice   **B)** Bronze
   C) Copper

6. The melting point of a substance is an example of a

   A) Physical property   **B)** Chemical property

7. In a physical change, only the _____ changes.

   A) State   **B)** Reactants
   C) Products

8. Ductile means

   A) Shiny   **B)** Bendable
   C) Stretchable   **D)** Breakable

9. Using the Internet or a reference book, find four physical properties and three chemical properties for one of the following substances: carbon dioxide, copper, or aluminum.

Lesson 2 CLASSIFICATION OF MATTER

Matter exists as
• pure substances
• mixtures

Pure substances
• elements
• compounds

Mixtures
• heterogeneous
• homogeneous

Scientists have divided the types of matter into sub-categories, based on distinct characteristics and properties. Remember that all matter exists as solids, liquids, or gases.

As well, all matter can be classified as pure substances or mixtures. There are two types of pure substances:
  •   elements
  •   compounds

There are two types of mixtures: heterogeneous and homogeneous.

  •   heterogeneous – three types
          – mechanical mixtures
          – suspensions
          – colloids (including emulsions)
  •   homogeneous mixtures – one type: solutions.

Types of Matter

The following diagram represents the different classifications of matter.

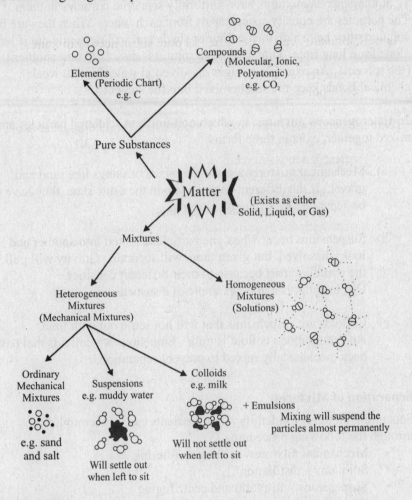

Elements
(Periodic Chart)
e.g. C

Compounds
(Molecular, Ionic,
Polyatomic)
e.g. CO_2

Pure Substances

Matter
(Exists as either
Solid, Liquid, or Gas)

Mixtures

Heterogeneous
Mixtures
(Mechanical Mixtures)

Homogeneous
Mixtures
(Solutions)

Ordinary
Mechanical
Mixtures

e.g. sand
and salt

Suspensions
e.g. muddy water

Will settle out
when left to sit

Colloids
e.g. milk

Will not settle out
when left to sit

+ Emulsions
Mixing will suspend the
particles almost permanently

Mixtures
• homogeneous
• heterogeneous

Solutions
• solute (salt)
• solvent (water)

Pure Substances

The simplest form of matter is called a pure substance. These substances cannot be decomposed by chemical changes. With the invention of the electron microscope, we can actually see images of the individual atoms or molecules of pure substances.

Pure substances are those with only one type of atom. These atoms, or *elements*, include substances such as gold, oxygen, and zinc and compounds with several joined atoms of different types, such as carbon dioxide and water.

• Elements are the simplest form of matter. They are represented on the Periodic Table. We now have about 115 discovered elements, each of which belongs to a family of elements that have similar characteristics. The noble gas family is one example (helium, neon, etc.).

• Compounds are groups of atoms with a unique set of chemical bonds and properties. Examples include table salt and water.

Mixtures

There are two types of mixtures: homogeneous and heterogeneous.

1. Homogeneous mixtures have uniformly scattered particles in them. The particles are equally spaced apart from each other. When they are in solution, they have a distinct colour or shade and will not settle out if left alone for a long time. One particle (a solute) is dissolved into another (the solvent). An example is sugar dissolved in water. Small weak chemical bonds keep the solute mixed into the solvent.

2. Heterogeneous mixtures, in which non-uniform scattered particles are mixed together, exist in three forms:

    a) Mechanical mixtures are simple mixes of things like sand and gravel. If the different particles are in the same state, they have to be separated by sifting or filtering.

    b) Suspensions occur when one particle is mixed into another and looks dissolved, but given time, will separate. Gravity will pull the particles apart because of their different densities. Dirt in water is a good example of a suspension.

    c) Colloids are suspensions that will not settle out with time. An example of a colloid is milk. Emulsions are colloids that have been mechanically mixed to prevent separation.

Separation of Mixtures

Separating mixtures to identify the ingredients can be accomplished through the following procedures.
- Mechanical mixtures – sifting or filtering
- Solutions – distillation
- Suspensions – filtration and centrifuging
- Colloidal solutions – centrifuging
- Compounds – chromatography
- Separation of mixtures separation

PRACTICE EXERCISE

1. Milk is a type of _____ solution.

2. Steel is a(n) _____.

3. Gold is a(n) _____.

4. Dirt is a(n) _____.

5. Beer is a(n) _____.

6. Rivers carry dirt by _____.

7. Red blood cells in plasma are an example of _____.

8. Which of the following characteristics best describes a solution?

   A) Cloudy colour   B) Distinct colour
   C) Particles settle out over time   D) Can be separated by filtration

9. Emulsions are

   A) Mechanical mixtures   B) Colloids
   C) Created to keep particles from separating D) All of the above

10. Give two examples of each of the following that you can find in your house and give their names.

   • Compounds

        1.

        2.

   • Heterogeneous mixtures

        1.

        2.

11. What are the two types of pure substances?

pure substances can be _____ and _____.

mixtures can be _____ and _____.

12. What are the two types of mixtures?

Lesson 3 THE SCIENTIFIC METHOD

According to the scientific method, when a problem or question arises, a hypothesis (idea of how it happened) is created to provide a solution or an explanation to the problem or question. A methodology for testing the hypothesis is developed based on the available technology (for example, there were no electron microscopes in the 1800s). Finally, an experiment is conducted that hopefully sheds some light on the answer to the problem or question. To be considered reliable, the results must be recorded and published. Lastly, carefully thought out conclusions are made.

Scientists explain the importance the findings have on the world around us. Other scientists that learn of the results must be able to repeat the experiment following the exact methods used in the first experiment. The experiment must be repeatable and the results must be verified before they are considered to be reliable.

The scientific method was widely adopted once reading and writing became common to all people. For example, the teaching of the *art* of chemistry became a *science*. In time, chemistry became its own discipline, as did mathematics, physics, biology, and medicine. Chemists are now found in all industries and in all fields medicine.

The following people are among the most notable chemists of the past and as a result of some of their findings, chemistry developed into a separate discipline.

1627-1691: Robert Boyle related pressure to volume, thus confirming the hypothesis that gases were made of atoms.

1743-1794: Antoine Lavoisier stated the Law of Conservation of Mass— "Mass is neither created nor destroyed when an experiment is done."

1766-1844: Sir John Dalton stated that all atoms were like small spheres, but of differing sizes and characteristics. All atoms of a pure substance were identical, and atoms combine in fixed ratios in the creation of new substances.

1856-1940: Joseph John Thomson discovered that electrons have charges. He theorized that atoms have positive and negative sub-particles and that atoms are in a ball-shaped configuration.

1871-1937: Ernest Rutherford determined that atoms have a positive (+) core that is $\dfrac{1}{1\,000}$ of the atom's size. The electrons surround the positive core.

1885-1962: Niels Bohr proposed that electrons exist in shells of varying energy levels around the positive core of an atom. Only the outer shell electrons react with each other.

All of these discoveries have led to the idea of Quantum Mechanics, where it is understood that each electron occupies a position in a cloud around the nucleus. The cloud shape changes at each energy level or orbit around the nucleus.

PRACTICE EXERCISE

1. The progression from alchemy to chemistry was accomplished in stages. Match the following discoveries or hypotheses with the appropriate scientist.

    A) ____ Atoms have positive core

    B) ____ Atoms are spheres

    C) ____ Electrons are negative

    D) ____ $P = \dfrac{1}{V}$

    E) ____ Energy levels of electrons

    F) ____ Mass is conserved in an experiment

    1. J. Dalton

    2. R. Boyle

    3. A. Lavoisier

    4. N. Bohr

    5. E. Rutherford

    6. J. J. Thomson

Lesson 4 PERIODIC TABLE OF THE ELEMENTS

NOTES

There are about 115 elements known to chemists. Only 90 are naturally occurring. The other 25 have been created by chemists. All elements are divided into one of three categories:

- metals
- non-metals
- metalloids

Each element has its own set of chemical and physical properties.

On the Periodic Table, each element is presented in a box with information about the element. Each element is represented by a letter(s), which is the symbol of the element. Along with this symbol and name, the atomic mass (bottom) and atomic number (top left) are presented. In some versions of the Periodic Table, densities, valence numbers, boiling points, melting points, and electronegativity numbers are included. You will study these in the future.

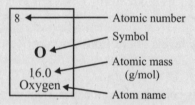

Each atom contains a nucleus with protons and neutrons. The atomic mass number is the total number of protons and neutrons in the nucleus. The nucleus takes up less than 1% of the atomic space.

An atom has an equal number of protons and electrons.

The electrons fill the remaining 99% of the atomic space. An atom has an equal number of protons and electrons.

Periodic Table of

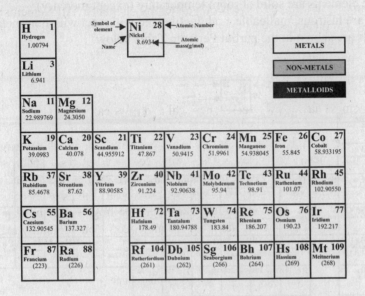

The Elements

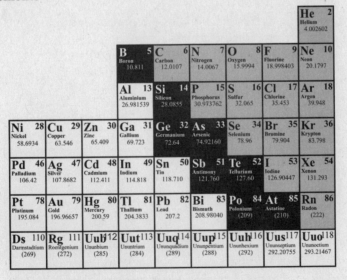

NOTES

Types of Elements

Metals

These elements are solid at room temperature (except mercury).
Most are lustrous, malleable, and ductile, and will react with non-metals.
Metals are shown in the partial Periodic Table below.

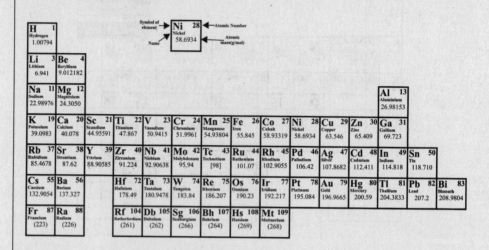

Non-Metals

These are elements that are grouped on the right side of the Periodic Table. Most of the non-metals exist as binary molecules, such as O_2, N_2, or F_2.

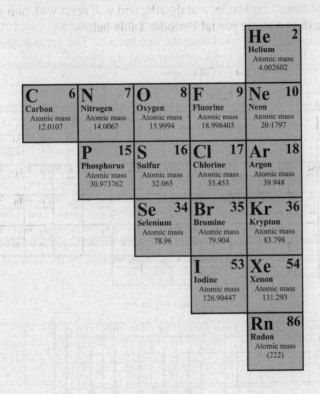

Metalloids

These elements have a mixture of both metal and non-metal properties and separate the metals and non-metals on the Periodic Table.

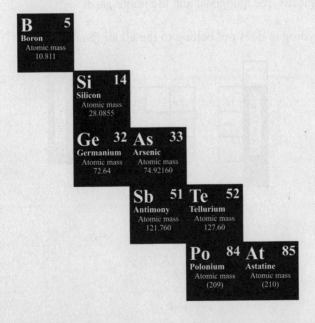

NOTES

Chemical Periods:
Each row in the Periodic Table represents a period.

Chemical Families:
Vertical columns on the Periodic Table represent chemical families.

Alkali family
- lithium   (Li)
- sodium   (Na)
- potassium   (K)
- rubidium   (Rb)
- cesium   (Cs)
- francium   (Fr)

Halogen family
- fluorine   (F)
- chlorine   (Cl)
- bromine   (Br)
- iodine   (I)
- astatine   (At)

Noble gas family
- helium   (He)
- neon   (Ne)
- argon   (Ar)
- krypton   (Kr)
- xenon   (Xe)
- radon   (Rn)

Groups

The elements are organized in the Periodic Table according to their properties. Each is given a short-form symbol.

There are seven periods of elements, each having one more electron energy orbital or electron shell level than the one before. The periods are represented by the seven horizontal rows of the Periodic Table.

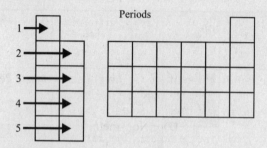

Chemical families contain elements that have similar chemical and physical properties. These families are represented by the vertical columns of the Periodic Table.

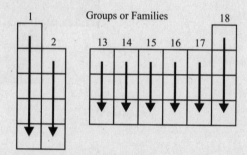

Alkali metals are all soft and shiny, react with water, and form a white solid when in a compound such as salt. The most well known families are the alkali metals, the halogens, and the noble gases.

Note: Hydrogen does not belong to the alkali family.

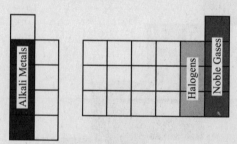

PRACTICE EXERCISE

1. List the three main classes of elements.

   •

   •

   •

2. What is the family name of the Group elements on the Periodic Table?

   A) Noble gases   B) Halogen

   C) Alkali   D) Non-metals

3. List three physical and one chemical property of sodium (Na).

   Physical Properties

   •

   •

   •

   Chemical Property

   •

4. Give the symbol for each of the first 11 elements of the Periodic Table in correct order (according to atomic number).

   1.   2.

   3.   4.

   5.   6.

   7.   8.

   9.   10.

   11.

5. Fill in the missing name or symbol for each of the following elements.

   a) Magnesium _____

   b) Copper _____

   c) Sulfur _____

   d) H _____

   e) Pb _____

   f) Ca _____

6. Enter the following elements in their correct position on the Periodic Table below.

   He   S   Al   Li
   K   C   O   Ar

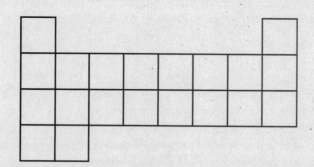

7. On the table below,

- place an X on the squares representing the halogens

- place an ✓ on the squares representing the alkali metals

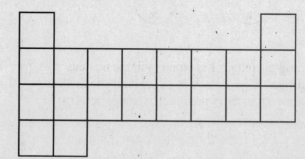

Lesson 5   ATOMS

An atom is made up of three types of particles:
- protons
- neutrons
- electrons

NOTES

Atoms are made up of
- protons
- neutrons
- electrons

The protons and neutrons are contained in the nucleus, while the electrons are outside the nucleus. The nucleus contains over 99% of the atom's mass, while the electrons occupy over 99% of the atom's volume.

Particle	Charge	Mass
Proton	positive charge	$1.7 \times 10-24$ g
Neutron	no charge	$1.7 \times 10-24$ g
Electron	negative charge	$9.1 \times 10-28$ g

It is believed that the major function of the neutrons is to keep the protons from repelling each other, as protons all have a positive charge.
Neutrons are like an insulator between protons. The electrons have enough room that they do not need an insulating material to keep them from repelling each other.

Isotopes

All atoms, even including the very simplest one, hydrogen, contain differing numbers of neutrons in the nucleus. Hydrogen will always contain one proton and one electron, but can have from zero to two neutrons. This is why hydrogen's atomic number is not exactly 1.00, but 1.01. The atomic number 1.01 is an average of all hydrogen atoms with varying neutrons. Hydrogen has three known isotopes, which are represented like this:

Isotopes – differing number of neutrons in an atom

Note:
- All three isotopes of hydrogen contain 1 proton (+) in the nucleus
- All three isotopes of hydrogen have 1 electron (–) outside the nucleus.
- The three isotopes of hydrogen differ in the number of neutrons (n) in the nucleus.

NOTES

To be able to calculate an atomic mass number, consider this example:

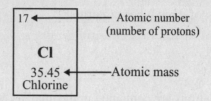

There are two naturally occurring isotopes of chlorine:

75.53% of all atoms are $_{17}^{35}$ Cl isotopes; the atomic number is 17, and the atomic mass is 35

24.47% of all atoms are $_{17}^{37}$ Cl isotopes; the atomic number is 17, and the atomic mass is 37

Notice that the atomic mass number differs in those isotopes: 35 and 37. The number of protons is always constant. It is the number of neutrons that increases the mass number. The unit of atomic mass is represented by the symbol μ.

μ is atomic mass unit

Consider a sample of 100 chlorine atoms,

Mass of 35 Cl isotopes   = 75.53 atoms × 35μ
      = 2 643.55μ
Mass of 37 Cl isotopes   = 24.47 atoms × 37μ
      = 905.39μ
Total mass of all 100 atoms   = 3 548.94μ
Average mass of each atom   = 35.49μ

Naming isotopes:

Chlorine – 37

↑

mass number

This average mass of each atom is what is recorded for each element in the Periodic Table. The value for chlorine above differs from the value in the Periodic Table because of rounding of the mass of each isotope.

To determine the number of neutrons of each element, round the atomic mass to the nearest whole number, and subtract the atomic number from the atomic mass; this leaves the number of neutrons, as shown below.

Example

$$_{24.31}^{12} \text{Mg} \Rightarrow {}_{24}^{12} \text{Mg} \text{ neutrons} = 12$$

$$_{55.85}^{26} \text{Fe} \Rightarrow {}_{56}^{26} \text{Fe} \text{ neutrons} = 30$$

All elements in the Periodic Table have isotopes that result in atomic numbers that are not whole numbers.

Electron energy levels

Electrons, which are on the outside of the nucleus, occupy different energy levels. Energy levels closest to the nucleus are always filled up first, and the more distant ones are filled when there is no room in a lower energy level.

This is very similar to a public gathering such as a concert or a sporting event. The seats close to the events are filled up first, while the more distant seats are filled last.

In an atom, the first energy level can hold two (2) electrons and the next level can hold up to eight (8) electrons.

Bohr Model

  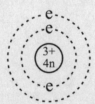 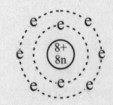

Quantum Mechanical Model

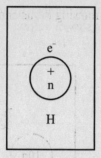 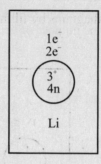 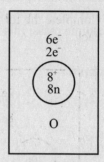

Mass number – sum of the number of protons and neutrons.

The mass number can be calculated from either model by adding the number of protons and neutrons. Therefore, the mass numbers of the above examples are:

- H is 1 proton + 1 neutron = 2
- Li is 3 protons + 4 neutrons = 7
- O is 8 protons + 8 neutrons = 16

PRACTICE EXERCISE

1. Complete the following diagrams by filling in the missing items and indicating the atomic mass of each:

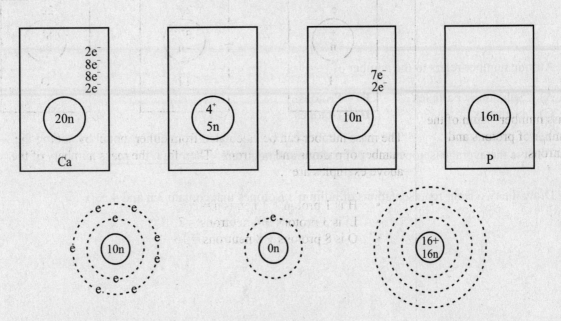

2. Using atomic masses rounded to the nearest whole number
   (e.g., sodium (Na) 22.99 rounds to 23, sulfur (S) 32.07 rounds to 32), complete the following table:

Element	Atomic Number	Protons	Electrons	Neutrons	Atomic Mass	Atom Representation
Ar	18	18	18	22	40	$^{40}_{18}Ar$
Li					7	
		8			16	
						$^{56}_{26}Fe$
			24		52	
H				0		
	13			14		
						$^{31}_{15}P$
Al			13	15		
	29			34		
						$^{4}_{2}He$

3. What is the mass of one proton? _____

4. What are the three primary subatomic particles that make up atoms?

_____   _____   _____

5. Atomic number refers to the number of

    A) Subatomic Particles   **B)** Protons
    C) Neutrons   **D)** Isotopes

6. What is the average isotope mass of an element known as? _____

7. Draw the two Bohr representations of lithium's isotopes that contain 3 n and 4 n.

8. An unknown element X has two isotopes. Of the first isotope, 80% has an atomic mass of 59 and the remaining 20% has a mass of 63. Calculate the average mass of the unknown element.

9. Using the Periodic Table below, determine the group and period for the atoms given in the chart below.

Li	Be			N	O		Ne
		Al				Cl	
	Ca						

Element	Period	Group
Ne		
Al		
N		
Li		
Cl		
Ca		
O		
Be		

Lesson 6   IONS

Because electrons are in orbit around the nucleus of an atom, they are in constant motion. A particle in motion can be deflected or pulled out of an orbit if the attractive force is great enough. Atoms can gain or lose electrons from their outer orbit. When the electrons are moved in or out of the atom's outer shell, the atom becomes electrically charged.
This is known as ionization.

Ions are formed by the gain or loss of electrons

The loss or gain of electrons from an atom disrupts the atomic balance between the positive protons and the negative electrons. This results in a positive (+) or negative (–) charge on the atom. If an atom gains an electron, there is one more electron than proton. For example, Cl will become Cl⁻. This negative ion is an *anion* and is typically found in non-metals on the right side of the Periodic Table of the elements.
When the electron is lost, the protons will outnumber the electrons, making a positive ion called a *cation*. Most metals from the left side of the Periodic Table form cations when they become ions.

Anions: – (gain electron(s))

Non-metals gain electron(s) to become negative (anion.)

Members of the noble gas family (group 8 on the Periodic Table) do not form ions.

Metals lose electron(s) to become positive (cation).

Members of the noble gas family do not ionize.

Naming Ions

Metals do not change names when ionized. Sodium is still called sodium in a compound. We simply add the word *ion* if it is alone.
Non-metals, however, have the last three letters of their name changed to "ide," thus chlorine becomes chloride.

Several metals such as copper (Cu) and iron (Fe) have the possibility of losing two or three electrons. They are then called copper (II) or (III) or iron (II) or (III). It is very difficult to lose more than three electrons because the remaining electrons are held tight to the nucleus.

PRACTICE EXERCISE

1. Complete the following table.

Atom	Ion	Electron gain	Electron loss
O	O^{2-}	$2e^-$	
Li	Li^+		$1e^-$
Mg			$2e^-$
	F^-	$1e^-$	
Ca			$2e^-$
Al	Al^{3+}		
N		$3e^-$	

2. Ions are charged atoms. The charge comes from the losing or gaining of

    A) A compound   **B)** An electron
    C) A neutron   **D)** A proton

Lesson 7 COMPOUNDS

To form compounds, at least two atoms must form ions. One atom will lose an electron, while the other atom will gain the electron. In this way two ions are formed, one positive and the other negative. Since opposite charges attract each other, the two ions will form a compound.

When sodium and chlorine are placed together, sodium will always give its outside electron to chlorine. This allows each to form an ion.

Octet Rule: Atoms want to have a complete outer energy level of 2 or 8 electrons. This can be accomplished by either losing or gaining electrons.

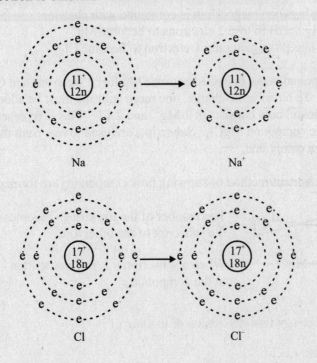

Na   Na⁺

Sodium loses an electron to become Na⁺.

Cl   Cl⁻

Chlorine gains an electron to become Cl⁻.

When combined, the two ions have opposite charges and are attracted to each other to form a compound called sodium chloride. In the naming of a compound, the positive ion is always given first, followed by the negative ion. Therefore, in this example the sodium is named before the chlorine (chloride).

Notice both ions have a full outside energy level.

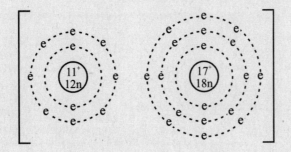

Ionic compounds contain a positive and a negative ion.

Compounds are always electrically neutral.

When two ions combine to form a compound, the compound is called an ionic compound. Ionic compounds are formed when metals (left side of the Periodic Table) combine with non-metals (right side of the Periodic Table).

In an ionic compound, the number of electrons lost will always equal the number of electrons gained. Therefore, the compound is electrically neutral.

For example, when magnesium is combined with chlorine:
- Mg needs to lose 2 electrons to become Mg^{2+}
- Cl needs to gain only 1 electron to become Cl^-

This compound is not balanced because Mg lost 2 electrons and Cl gained only one. To balance the charge, one more chlorine must be added. The compound now consists of 1 Mg^{2+} and 2 Cl^-. This is represented by writing the compound $MgCl_2$. Subscripts are used to represent the number of ions in a compound.

Here is a shortcut method of showing how compounds are formed:

$$Mg^{2+} \quad + \quad Cl^-$$

The number of the ion charge becomes the subscript of the other ion.

$Mg_1Cl_2 = MgCl_2$

When a subscript is 1, it is not written in the compound.

PRACTICE EXERCISE

1. In the table below, write the compound formula and name the compound when the following elements are combined. An example has been done for you.

Elements	Positive ion formed	Negative ion formed	Compound Formula	Compound Name
K + Cl	K^+	Cl^-	KCl	potassium chloride
Al + F				
Li + O				
Be + N				
Na + O				
K + N				
Ca + Br				
Mg + I				

Lesson 8 NAMING AND WRITING FORMULAS WITH IONS THAT HAVE MULTIPLE CHARGES

This method is also known as the STOCK system.

Some metals form two ions with different charges. The IUPAC system distinguishes between these two ions by using a Roman numeral in the name of the compound to indicate which ion it is.

Example 1

What is the formula for iron (III) oxide?

Solution

The iron (III) ion is Fe^{3+} and the oxide ion is O^{2-}. The least common multiple needs to be found to see how many atoms of each substance is in the compound. The least common multiple of 3 and 2 is 6.

$$\frac{6}{3} = 2 \text{ and } \frac{6}{2} = 3$$

Therefore, the formula is Fe_2O_3.

The compound is electrically neutral with a positive charge of 6+ and a negative charge of 6–.

Example 2

What is the name of SnI_4?

Solution

I^- is the symbol for the iodide ion and Sn^{4+} is the symbol for the tin (IV) ion. (The charge must be 4+ to balance the negative charge.)

Therefore, the name is tin (IV) iodide.

PRACTICE EXERCISE

1. Write the ion charges and names for the following compounds. The first one is done for you.

Compound Formula	Metal Ion Charge	Non-Metal Ion Charge	Name
$NiCl_3$	Ni^{3+}	Cl^-	nickel (III) chloride
MnO			
Cr_2O_3			
$CuCl_2$			
PbO_2			
FeO			

2. Write formulas for the following compounds

Compound Name	Compound Formula
nickel (II) iodide	
lead (II) nitride	
tin (IV) oxide	
antimony (III) chloride	
copper (II) oxide	

Lesson 9   POLYATOMIC IONS (COMPLEX IONS)

NOTES

Polyatomic ions are naturally occurring molecules that act as ions. Only one, ammonia (NH_4^+), acts like an anion. All of the others are cations and have a 1^-, 2^- or 3^- charge. When these molecules act as ions, they normally remain intact.

The most common polyatomic ions are listed below.

Those polyatomic ions should be memorized.

ammonium	NH_4^+
carbonate	CO_3^{2-}
chlorate	ClO_3^-
dihydrogen phosphate	$H_2PO_4^-$
hydrogen carbonate	HCO_3^-
hydroxide	OH^-
nitrate	NO_3^-
nitrite	NO_2^-
permanganate	MnO_4^-
phosphate	PO_4^{3-}
sulfate	SO_4^{2-}
sulfite	SO_3^{2-}

Remember: these are ions and do not exist alone in nature.

Naming Polyatomic Compounds

When polyatomic ions form compounds, the positive ion is named first, followed by the negative ion; e.g., potassium sulfate, K_2SO_4, and sodium phosphate, Na_3PO_4.

NO_2^- has one less oxygen atom than NO_3^-. The one with the lesser number of oxygen atoms has an "ite" ending, while the one with the greater number of oxygen atoms has an "ate" ending. Therefore, NO_2^- is nitrite, while NO_3^- is nitrate. Sulfate is SO_4^{2-}, while SO_3^{2-} is sulfite.

Notice that both NO_2^- and NO_3^- are listed in the table.

When more than one polyatomic ion is needed in a compound, brackets are used around the polyatomic ion with the subscript to denote the number of ions needed. Two examples are shown below.

Magnesium and hydroxide ion: Mg^{2+} + OH^- → $Mg(OH)^2$
Ammonium ion and sulfate ion: NH_4^+ + SO_4^{2-} → $(NH_4)_2SO_4$

PRACTICE EXERCISE

1. Complete the following chart.

Compound	Cation	Anion	Formula
Barium sulfate	Ba^{2+}	SO_4^{2-}	$BaSO_4$
Aluminum bromide			$AlBr_2$
	Zn^{2+}	O^{2-}	
			$MgCl_2$
	Ca^{2+}	OH^-	
Sodium chlorate			
			NH_4NO_3

2. Name the following compounds.

   a) Na_2CO_3 _____

   b) $MgSO_4$ _____

   c) $MgSO_3$ _____

3. Name five polyatomic ions and write their formulas, showing their charge.

   a) _____ _____

   b) _____ _____

   c) _____ _____

   d) _____ _____

   e) _____ _____

Lesson 10   MOLECULAR COMPOUNDS

NOTES

Molecular compounds are compounds in which bonds exist between two non-metals. For example and O_2 and CO_2:

There are three types of molecular compounds.

These molecular compounds should be memorized.

- Monoatomic – compounds comprised of only one atom, such as carbon (C), and the noble gases (He and Ne)
- Diatomic – Compounds comprised of two atoms, such as H_2 , N_2, O_2, F_2, Cl_2, Br_2, and I_2
- Polyatomic – Compounds comprised of more than two atoms, such as CO_2, SO_2, and H_2O

The molecules of molecular compounds are internally held together with covalent bonds (which involves sharing electrons). A molecular bond is strong. There is little attractive force between molecules however, therefore, melting points are low and they form crystals that do not hold their shape when heated (e.g., ice). These molecules are electrically neutral when in solid or liquid states.

The hydrogen molecule (H_2) forms a covalent bond when a hydrogen atom's one electron is shared with another hydrogen atom. Since the first energy level can only accommodate two electrons, each hydrogen acts as if it has a complete energy level.

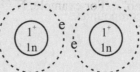

Water is a special case because of its bent configuration and the fact that it does not share its electrons equally. The oxygen atom pulls the electrons that it shares with the two hydrogen atoms closer to its nucleus, thereby creating a positive end and a negative end. The molecule now has polarity and is considered to have a polar covalent bond. This raises the boiling and melting points of the compound. This configuration also forms a solid six-sided crystal that is less dense than liquid water. This allows ice to float.

It is very easy to test the polarity of water. Take a plastic strip (such as a credit card) and put a charge on it by rubbing it with a paper towel. Place it beside a fine stream of water from a tap. Notice how the water bends toward the plastic.

Naming Molecular Compounds

For compounds without hydrogen, the first atom retains its normal name. The second atom usually ends in "ide." For example, when carbon combines with oxygen, carbon remains carbon and oxygen is changed to oxide. Then, a prefix signifying the number of atoms present is added to either or both atoms. The most common prefixes are used below. Usually, mono is not used except for a few compounds, such as CO - carbon monoxide.

- CO - carbon monoxide
- CO_2 - carbon dioxide
- H_2O - dihydrogen oxide (common name for water)
- N_2O_3 - dinitrogen trioxide

Common prefixes:
one — mono
two — di
three — tri

Prefixes

Mono:	1	Hexa:	6
Di:	2	Hepta:	7
Tri:	3	Octa:	8
Tetra:	4	Nona:	9
Penta:	5	Deca:	10

If the name of the element begins with a vowel, drop the final "a" in the prefix (or the "o" in "mono"). For example, N_2O_5 is dinitrogen pentoxide, not dinitrogen pentaoxide.

Naming of Molecules that Contain Hydrogen

As a result of the common usage of the following compounds, these molecules have been given different names over a period of time. These names should be memorized.

$H_2O_{(l)}$ – water

$H_2O_{2(l)}$ - hydrogen peroxide

These compounds should be memorized.

$NH_{3(g)}$ – ammonia

$C_{12}H_{22}O_{11(s)}$ – sucrose

$C_6H_{12}O_{6(s)}$ – glucose

$H_2S_{(g)}$ - hydrogen sulfide

$CH_{4(g)}$ – methane

$C_3H_{8(g)}$ – propane

$CH_3OH_{(l)}$ – methanol

$CH_3COOH_{(aq)}$ - acetic acid (vinegar)

$C_2H_5OH_{(l)}$ - ethanol

PRACTICE EXERCISE

1. What type of atoms form molecular bonds?

   A) Metals

   B) Non-metals

   C) Metals and non-metals

   D) Metalloids

2. Write the prefixes that represent the following numerical values.

   a) 2 _____

   b) 3 _____

   c) 4 _____

   d) 5 _____

3. Complete the following chart.

Compound Formula	Common Name
H_2O	water
CH_4	
	hydrogen peroxide
H_2S	
	glucose
	methanol

4. Write the formulas of the compounds given in the chart below.

Compound Name	Compound Formula
sulfur dioxide	SO_2
carbon monoxide	
dihydrogen sulfide	
sulfur dichloride	
tetraphosphorus decaoxide	

5. Write the names of the following compounds

Compound Formula	Name
SiO_2	silicon dioxide
OCl_2	
SO_3	
CO_2	
NO_2	

44

Lesson 11 PROPERTIES OF IONIC COMPOUNDS

Five properties that ionic compounds have in common is that they all

- have high melting points
- are solid at room temperature
- form crystal lattices
- will dissolve in water to a certain extent
- when dissolved in water, the solution will conduct an electric current

The following rules outline the solubility of certain ions in water.

- Group I metals and NH_4^+, H^+, ClO_3^-, NO_3^-, and ClO_4^- are all soluble in water

- CH_3COO^- when in compounds is soluble in water except when added to Ag^+

- Br^-, Cl^-, and I^- are soluble in water except when added to Ag^+, Pb^{2+}, and Cu^+.

- SO_4^{2-} is soluble in water unless mixed with Ca^{2+}, Sr^{2+}, Ba^{2+}, Ra^{2+}, Pb^{2+}, or Ag^+

- OH^- is soluble in water when combined with Group I elements, NH_4^+, Sr^{2+}, or Ba^{2+}.

- PO_4^{3-}, SO_3^{2-}, and CO_3^{2-} are soluble in water only when added to Group I elements and NH_4^+

The following chart summarizes the rules listed above.

Ion	Group IA NH_4^+ H^+	ClO_3^- NO_3^- ClO_4^-	CH_3COO^-	Cl^- Br^- I^-	SO_4^{2-}	S^{2-}	OH^-	PO_4^{3-} SO_3^{2-} CO_3^{2-}
Solubility greater than or equal to 0.1 mol/L (very soluble)	all	all	most	most	most	Group IA Group IIA NH_4^+	Group IA NH_4^+ Sr^{2+} Ba^{2+} Tl^+	NH_4^+ Group IA
Solubility less than 0.1 mol/L (slightly soluble)	none	none	Ag^+ Hg^+	Ag^+ Pb^{2+} Hg^+ Cu^+ Tl^+	Ca^{2+} Sr^{2+} Ba^{2+} Ra^{2+} Pb^{2+} Ag^+	most	most	most

PRACTICE EXERCISE

1. Complete the following table.

Compound Name	Compound Formula	Solubility in Water
sodium chloride	NaCl	Yes, all group I metals are soluble.
	$AgNO_3$	
magnesium sulfate		
	$AlCl_3$	
calcium sulfate		
	$Be(OH)_2$	
	Na_3PO_4	
lithium chlorate		

Lesson 12 STATES OF CHEMICAL REACTIONS

NOTES

The following rules outline the states of physical substances in chemical reactions. Assume that all reactions are at room temperature unless otherwise stated.

1. All metals except mercury ($Hg_{(l)}$) are solids.

2. Most diatomic elements are gases except $Br_{2(l)}$ and $I_{2(s)}$.

3. Sulfur, phosphorous, and carbon are solids.

4. All ionic compounds are solid except when in water, where they dissolve and become aqueous $_{(aq)}$.

5. Small molecular compounds are gases $_{(g)}$.

From this point on, all equations are to be balanced and two states of matter expressed for each substance.

PRACTICE EXERCISE

Write the physical state of each of the following substances at room temperature.

1. K

2. CO_2

3. S_8

4. I_2

5. NaCl

6. Fe

7. CH_4

8. A solution of KNO_3

Lesson 13 ACIDS AND BASES

NOTES

Arrhenius, a chemist from the 19th century, proposed that any substance that produces hydrogen ions (H^+) when dissolved in water should be called an acid. He also proposed that when a substance produces hydroxide ions (OH^-) when dissolved in water, it should be called a base.

An acid produces H^+ ions in water.

For example, if $HCl_{(g)}$ is added to water, then the H^+ ion will separate from the Cl^- ion and form a powerful acid (hydrochloric acid or stomach acid).

A base produces OH^- ions in water.

If $NaOH_{(s)}$ is added to water, then the OH^- will separate from the Na^+ ion and form a powerful base (sodium hydroxide).

Many chemicals used on a daily basis are acids or bases. For example, vinegar and vitamin C are both acids.

Substances such as baking powder, antacid tablets, and most soaps are all bases.

Some chemical and physical properties of acids and bases are listed below.

Property	Acid	Base
Taste	sour	bitter
Feel	wet	slippery
Reaction with Mg	produces $H_{2(g)}$	no reaction
Indicator	turns blue litmus red	turns red litmus blue
Conductive	yes	yes
pH	<7	>7

Litmus paper is used to determine the H^+ ion concentration, $[H^+]$, of solutions. The measurement of this concentration is called pH.
The pH scale goes from 1 to 14. The most acidic concentrations are at pH 1 and the weakest acids (strongest bases) are at pH 14. Each number change represents a ten-fold change in the H^+ ion concentration.
For example, a pH of 1 is 10 times stronger than a pH of 2, and a pH of 3 is 10 times stronger than a pH of 4.

Testing pH

Two easy testing methods exist for determining pH.

- The universal indicator is a mixture of several liquid indicators that turn different colours when exposed to hydrogen ions (H^+). Liquid indicator will turn orange if the pH is 1, green if the solution is neutral (pH 7), and blue if the pH is near 14.

- The second indicator is called litmus paper. There are two types: red and blue. In an acidic solution, blue litmus paper turn red. In a basic solution, red litmus paper will turn blue.

Acids: pH 1–7
The lower the pH, the stronger the acid.
Bases: pH 7–14
The higher the pH, the stronger the base.

Naming Acids

Binary Acids have H^+ ions followed by a second non-metal ending in "ic". To name these substances, change the "hydrogen" to "hydro," and the "ide" ending of the non-metal to "ic." For example, hydrogen chloride ($HCl_{(aq)}$) becomes hydrochloric acid.

Oxyacids have a H^+ ion followed by a polyatomic ion. The endings for the name of the ions is determined by the number of oxygen atoms. In the ions with less oxygen, the ending is "ous," and where the concentration is greater, the suffix is "ic." The hydrogen name is dropped.
As well, "hydro" is not used.

Binary acids always end in "ic."

Examples

- hydrogen sulfate ($H_2SO_{4(aq)}$) becomes sulfuric acid.
- hydrogen sulfite ($H_2SO_{3(aq)}$) becomes sulfurous acid.

Oxyacids:
"ate" endings end in "ic"
"ite" endings end in "ous"

Common Acids

- Hydrochloric acid ($HCl_{(aq)}$) - muriatic acid, found in your stomach
- Sulfuric acid ($H_2SO_{4(aq)}$) - battery acid
- Acetic acid $CH_3COOH_{(aq)}$ - vinegar

NOTES

The name of a base always ends in "hydroxide."

Naming Bases

The name of a base always ends in "hydroxide," which indicates the presence of OH^- ions. For example, the base $NaOH_{(aq)}$ is sodium hydroxide.

COMMON BASES.

• Sodium hydroxide ($NaOH_{(aq)}$) - also called caustic soda
• Ammonium hydroxide ($NH_4OH_{(aq)}$) - the active ingredient of window cleaners
• Calcium hydroxide ($Ca(OH)_{2(s)}$) - is called coke and is used in making steel
• Magnesium hydroxide ($Mg(OH)_{2(aq)}$) and aluminum hydroxide ($Al(OH)_{3(aq)}$) - are used as antacids and to clean water

Neutralization

When acids and bases are combined, they neutralize each other and form a salt and water.

Acid rain added to calcium hydroxide forms calcium sulfate and water. This is a neutralization reaction. Calcium sulfate is the salt that is formed.

$$Ca(OH)_{2(aq)} + H_2SO_{4(aq)} \rightarrow CaSO_{4(s)} + 2H_2O_{(l)}$$
$\quad$ base $\qquad\qquad$ acid $\qquad$ salt $\qquad\quad$ water

PRACTICE EXERCISE

1. Complete the following table.

Acid Name	Binary or Oxy	Formula
Hydrobromic acid	binary	$HBr_{(aq)}$
Sulfurous acid		
Hydrochloric acid		
		$HNO_{3(aq)}$
		$HF_{(aq)}$
Nitrous acid		

2. Complete the following table.

Base Name	Formula
potassium hydroxide	$KOH_{(aq)}$
ammonium hydroxide	
barium hydroxide	
	$LiOH_{(aq)}$
sodium hydroxide	

3. Name the following compounds and classify them as an acid, base, ionic compounds, or molecular composed.

Compound Formula	Compound Name	Acid, Base, Ionic Compound, Molecular Compound
$Ca(NO_3)_{2(s)}$	calcium nitrate	ionic compound
$H_2SO_{4(aq)}$		
$(NH_4)_2SO_{3(aq)}$		
$NaCl_{(aq)}$		
$P_2O_{5(g)}$		
$KOH_{(aq)}$		

4. When an acid is added to water, it releases

   A) OH atoms   **B)** OH^- ions
   C) H atoms   **D)** H^+ ions

5. Which of the following substances is an example of an acid?

   A) Baking powder   **B)** Ammonia
   C) Lemon juice   **D)** Drain cleaner

6. Red litmus paper turns blue when dipped into

   A) An acid   **B)** A base
   C) Water   **D)** A salt solution

54

7. A universal indicator turns blue in

   A) An acid   **B)** A base
   C) A neutral solution   **D)** Water

8. Complete the following chart.

Name	Formula	Use
	$Mg(OH)_{2(aq)}$	
Caustic soda		
		Window cleaner

9. Liquids with a pH of 7 are

   A) Neutral   **B)** Acidic
   C) Basic

10. Explain why the conductivity of water changes when $HCl_{(aq)}$ is added to it.

11. Which is stronger, an acid with pH 2 or an acid with pH 5?

12. Write the formula for each of the following compounds and identify each as an acid, base, ionic compound, or molecular compound.

Name	Formula	Acid, Base, Ionic Compound, Molecular Compound
dinitrogen trioxide	N_2O_3	Molecular
magnesium sulfide		
hydrobromic acid		
glucose		
ammonium sulfate		
nitric acid		

13. Complete the following table and indicate which acids are binary acids and which are oxyacids.

Name	Formula	Binary Acid or Oxyacid
hydrochloric acid	$HCl_{(aq)}$	Binary acid
nitric acid		
	$H_3BO_{3(aq)}$	
phosphoric acid		
	$H_2SO_{4(aq)}$	

Lesson 14   CHEMICAL EQUATIONS

Once the basics of chemical reactions are understood, safe experiments can be conducted to produce new products. There are many types of reactions, but all can be classified as either exothermic (energy-producing reactions) or endothermic (energy-consuming reactions).

Both endothermic and exothermic reactions need energy to get started, but exothermic reactions will continue on without the need for additional energy. Most exothermic reactions need to be ignited before energy will be released at room temperature.

Exothermic — energy given off as heat

- An exothermic reaction
  $$CH_{4(g)} + O_{2(g)} \rightarrow CO_{2(g)} + H_2O_{(g)} + energy$$

- An endothermic reaction
  $$N_{2(g)} + O_{2(g)} + energy \rightarrow 2NO_{(g)}$$

Endothermic — energy taken in as heat

Changes of state sometimes occur during chemical reactions.
Remember that in any chemical reaction, there is always conservation of mass and energy. The amount of substance started with equals the amount produced.

Chemical Equations

Chemical equations are used to represent chemical reactions with symbols and formulas that represent the elements and compounds involved.
Equations must be balanced to show that atoms (and, therefore, mass) are conserved.

Coefficient — the number in front of a symbol; represents the number of atoms or molecules

- Coefficient - the number in front of a chemical, e.g., 3Na.
  In this example, the 3 is a coefficient. It represents the number of atoms or molecules of the chemical.

- Subscript - the small number after a chemical, e.g. N_2O_5.
  In this example, both the 2 and 5 are subscripts. They represent the amount of each atom in the compound.

Subscript — the number behind a symbol; represents the amount of each atom

The following elements never exist as single atoms. They are represented as shown.:

H_2	N_2
O_2	F_2
Cl_2	Br_2
I_2	At_2
S_8	P_4

Balancing Chemical Equations

To show how to balance a chemical equation, the example of the decomposition of dinitrogen pentoxide gas will be used.
Dinitrogen pentoxide gas decomposes into two elements: nitrogen gas and oxygen gas.

Step 1   Represent the reactant and products with formulas.

$$N_2O_{5(s)} \rightarrow N_{2(g)} + O_{2(g)}$$

Step 2   When there is an odd number of atoms of an element on one side and an even number on the other side, find a common multiple. For oxygen, the common multiple of 5 and 2 is 10.

Step 3   Multiply each formula by a coefficient to represent the same number of atoms of oxygen on both sides
(using the least common multiple). So, because in N_2O_5 there are 5 oxygen atoms, the coefficient is 2 (as $5 \times 2 = 10$).

$$2N_2O_{5(s)} \rightarrow N_{2(g)} + 5O_{2(g)}$$

Step 4   Add coefficients to the remaining formulas to balance the remaining atoms. There must be 4 atoms of nitrogen represented on both sides.

$$2N_2O_{5(s)} \rightarrow 2N_{2(g)} + 5O_{2(g)}$$

Step 5   Check to make sure all atoms are balanced.
Left side: Right side:
4 N and 10 O   4 N and 10 O

For example, in the following equation, check the number of atoms of both the reactant side and the product side to make sure the equation is balanced.

$$2Na_{(s)} + 2H_2O_{(l)} \rightarrow 2NaOH_{(aq)} + H_{2(g)}$$

Solution

L.S.	R.S.
2Na	2Na
4H	2H + 2H = 4H
2O	2O

NOTE: In $2H_2O$, the coefficient 2 is multiplied by the subscript 2 to get 4 hydrogen.

PRACTICE EXERCISE

1. In the following equations, check the number of atoms of both the reactant and product sides to make sure the equations are balanced.

a) $4\,Al_{(s)} + 3O_{2(g)} \rightarrow 2Al_2O_{3(s)}$

b) $Cl_{2(g)} + 2KI_{(aq)} \rightarrow I_{2(s)} + 2KCl_{(aq)}$

c) $NH_{3(g)} + HNO_{3(aq)} \rightarrow NH_4NO_{3(aq)}$

d) $3H_2SO_{4(aq)} + Ca_3(PO_4)_{2(aq)} \rightarrow 2H_3PO_{4(aq)} + 3CaSO_{4(aq)}$

2. Balance the following equations

   a) $Al_{(s)} + F_{2(g)} \rightarrow AlF_{3(s)}$

   b) $K_{(s)} + O_{2(g)} \rightarrow K_2O_{(s)}$

   c) $Na_{(s)} + Cl_{2(g)} \rightarrow NaCl_{(s)}$

   d) $H_2O_{(l)} \rightarrow O_{2(g)} + H_{2(g)}$

   e) $CH_{4(g)} + O_{2(g)} \rightarrow CO_{2(g)} + H_2O_{(g)}$

Lesson 15 CHEMICAL REACTION TYPES

There are five basic types of reactions in chemistry.

Formation Reactions (F)

Two separate elements combine to form one new compound.
    $a + b \rightarrow ab$
    reactant + reactant = product

For example, sodium metal added to chlorine gas reacts to make sodium chloride solid.

$$2Na_{(s)} + Cl_{2(g)} \rightarrow 2NaCl_{(s)}$$

Decomposition Reactions (D)

A compound decomposes to form two separate elements.
    $ab \rightarrow a + b$

For example, water is decomposed by an electric current into hydrogen gas and oxygen gas.

$$2H_2O_{(l)} \rightarrow 2H_{2(g)} + O_{2(g)}$$

Single Replacement Reactions (SR)

An element reacts with a compound to form a new compound and an element.
    $a + bc \rightarrow b + ac$

For example, zinc metal reacts with copper (II) nitrate solution to produce copper metal and zinc nitrate solution.

$$Zn_{(s)} + Cu(NO_3)_{2(aq)} \rightarrow Cu_{(s)} + Zn(NO_3)_{2(aq)}$$

Double Replacement Reactions (DR)

In a double replacement reaction, positive ions in each compound trade places to form two new compounds.
    $ab + cd \rightarrow ad + cb$

For example, when hydrochloric acid is mixed with sodium hydroxide solution, a sodium chloride solution and liquid water are produced.

$$HCl_{(aq)} + 2NaOH_{(aq)} \rightarrow NaCl_{(aq)} + H_2O_{(l)}$$

Hint: Sometimes $H_2O_{(l)}$ is written as $HOH_{(l)}$.

NOTES

Types of Reactions
- Formation
- Decomposition
- Single Replacement
- Double Replacement
- Combustion

NOTES

Exothermic:
reaction gives off heat
Endothermic:
reaction needs heat to occur

Combustion Reactions (C)

A compound reacts with oxygen to form the most common oxide.
O_2 reacts with carbon → $CO_{2(g)}$
O_2 reacts with hydrogen → $H_2O_{(g)}$

For example, methane gas reacts with oxygen gas to produce carbon dioxide gas and water vapour.

$$CH_{4(g)} + 2O_{2(g)} \rightarrow CO_{2(g)} + 2H_2O_{(g)}$$

OXYGEN REACTIONS

Oxygen makes up almost 20% of the air on Earth, but it plays a far greater role in the life processes of all living things. Oxygen is involved in three major sub-types of chemical reactions. They are combustion reactions, corrosion reactions, and cellular respiration.

Combustion Reactions

When oxygen gas is added to wood, the wood will not automatically burn. Energy needs to be added to ignite the wood. Once the wood temperature is high enough, oxygen will react with it to produce both water vapour and carbon dioxide gas. The heat that is released far exceeds the amount needed to start the combustion, so this reaction is exothermic.

When wet wood is burned, water vapour comes off the wood as the reaction occurs. The dark smoke that accompanies the heat and water vapour is just unburned particles of the wood that have not been totally reacted in the fire.

The combustion reaction that is represented by the equation:

$$CH_{4(s)} + 2O_{2(g)} \rightarrow 2H_2O_{(g)} + CO_{2(g)}$$

The use of this reaction is the basis of modern industry. It powers the engines that make cars move and factories run.

Corrosion Reactions

When metals are exposed to the open air, they react slowly with the oxygen present in the air. These metals then form oxides such as rust. To prevent corrosion, metals can be coated with paint or their surfaces can be galvanized with non-rusting alloys.

The corrosion (rusting) reaction that is represented by the equation:

$$2Fe_{(s)} + O_{2(g)} + 2H_2O_{(l)} \rightarrow 2Fe(OH)_{2(s)}$$

(Iron) (Iron (II) hydroxide)

The reaction that occurs when oxygen reacts with the iron present in our red blood cells. When exposed to air, our blood turns red.
Before this exposure, our blood is more of a blue color.

Cellular Respiration

As we consume food, the molecules are broken down into: proteins, fats, and carbohydrates, which must be converted into glucose so they become energy that can be used in our cells. Once a cell receives glucose, the cell will store the glucose. When the glucose is needed, it is burned in the mitochondria of the cell to produce carbon dioxide (CO_2), water, and energy. The energy is captured in the bonds of a molecule called ATP (adenosine triphosphate). This process is called *cellular respiration*. It is represented by the equation

$$C_6H_{12}O_{6(s)} + 6O_{2(g)} \rightarrow 6CO_{2(g)} + 6H_2O_{(l)} + \text{energy}$$

The energy is stored in ATP molecules and transported to other parts of the cell and body when needed.

ACTIVITY

Title
Types of Chemical Reactions: Simple Composition

Problem
What are the properties of the compound produced by the reaction of magnesium burning in air?

Materials
magnesium ribbon	tongs
beaker	Bunsen burner
water	

Procedure

1. Use tongs to hold the magnesium ribbon while igniting it in the Bunsen burner.

2. Hold the burning magnesium in a beaker to collect a sample of the product.

3. Observe the product. Note its colour, phase, textures and solubility in water.

   Safety Precaution: AVOID LOOKING DIRECTLY AT THE BURNING MAGNESIUM.

Observations:

	Colour	Phase	Texture	Solubility in Water
Before Procedure				
After Procedure				

Conclusion:

EXPANSION QUESTIONS FOR ACTIVITY

1. What evidence was observed to indicate that a chemical reaction occurred?

2. Write the balanced chemical equation for the observed chemical reaction.

3. Name the product formed in this chemical reaction.

4. Suggest another possible chemical reaction that might be occurring in this experiment.
    Write a balanced equation for this reaction.

PRACTICE EXERCISE

For each of the following reactions, write a balanced equation.

1. Carbon solid added to oxygen gas reacts to form carbon dioxide gas (formation reaction).

2. Sulfur solid reacts with chlorine gas to form sulfur dichloride gas (formation reaction).

    (Hint: Sulfur by itself is written S_8.)

3. Iron solid reacts in the presence of oxygen gas to form iron (III) oxide solid (formation reaction).

    (Hint: Iron (III) oxide is Fe_2O_3.)

4. Methane gas decomposes into solid carbon and hydrogen gas (decomposition reaction).

5. Heating iron (II) oxide solid decomposes it into iron metal and oxygen gas (decomposition reaction).

    (Hint: Iron (II) oxide is $FeO_{(s)}$.)

6. Mercury (II) oxide solid decomposes into mercury liquid and oxygen gas (decomposition reaction).

7. Aluminum metal is put in a sodium chloride solution and produces sodium metal and aluminum chloride solution. (Single replacement reaction)

8. When iron metal is put into a mercury (II) oxide solution, an iron (III) oxide solution and mercury are produced. (Single replacement reaction)

9. Calcium metal is put into a solution of lithium hydroxide; pure lithium metal and a solution of calcium hydroxide are produced. (Single replacement reaction)

10. Sodium chloride solution is mixed with a zinc nitrate solution, and sodium nitrate solution and zinc chloride solution are produced. (Double replacement reaction)

11. Potassium permanganate solution is mixed with ammonium sulfate solution, producing potassium sulfate solution and ammonium permanganate solution. (Double replacement reaction)

12. When a sodium chloride solution is mixed with zinc acetate, a sodium acetate solution and zinc chloride solution are produced.

13. Propane ($C_3H_{8(g)}$) burns in oxygen gas to produce carbon dioxide gas and water vapour.

14. Gasoline (C_8H_{18}) is burned in an engine, and carbon dioxide gas and water vapour are produced.

15. When butane (C_4H_{10}) is burned in a torch, carbon dioxide gas and water vapour are produced.

16. Write a combustion reaction equation involving methanol ($CH_3OH_{(l)}$).

17.. Write a balanced reaction equation showing the formation of rust.

18. Write the balanced chemical reaction equation for cellular respiration.

19. For each of the following equations, identify the type of reaction (from the five types: formation (F), decomposition (D), single replacement (SR), double replacement (DR), and combustion (C)) and add coefficients to balance the equation.

a) ___F___ ___ $N_{2(g)}$ + _2_ $H_{2(g)}$ → _2_ $NH_{2(g)}$

b) ____ ___ $Na_{(s)}$ + ___ $Cl_{2(g)}$ → ___ $NaCl_{(s)}$

c) ____ ___ $H_2O_{(l)}$ → ___ $H_{2(g)}$ + ___ $O_{2(g)}$

d) ____ ___ $Na_{(s)}$ + ___ $H_2O_{(l)}$ → ___ $NaOH_{(aq)}$ + ___ $H_{2(g)}$

e) ____ ___ $Zn_{(s)}$ + ___ $HCl_{(aq)}$ → ___ $ZnCl_{2(aq)}$ + ___ $H_{2(g)}$

f) ____ ___ $CH_{4(g)}$ + ___ $O_{2(g)}$ → ___ $CO_{2(g)}$ + ___ $H_2O_{(g)}$

g) ____ ___ $P_{4(s)}$ + ___ $Cl_{2(g)}$ → ___ $PCl_{5(s)}$

h) ____ ___ $CoCl_{2(aq)}$ + ___ $Na_{(s)}$ → ___ $NaCl_{(aq)}$ + ___ $Co_{(s)}$

i) ____ ___ $Na_3PO_{4(aq)}$ + ___ $MgCl_{2(aq)}$ → ___ $Mg_3(PO_4)_{2(s)}$ + ___ $NaCl_{2(aq)}$

j) ____ ___ $C_4H_{2(g)}$ + ___ $O_{2(g)}$ → ___ $CO_{2(g)}$ + ___ $H_2O_{(g)}$

k) ____ ___ $P_2O_{5(s)}$ → ___ $P_{4(s)}$ + ___ $O_{2(g)}$

l) ____ ___ $Al_{(s)}$ + ___ $Cu(NO_2)_{2(aq)}$ → ___ $Cu_{(s)}$ + ___ $Al(NO_2)_{3(aq)}$

m) ____ ___ $CaC_{2(s)}$ + ___ $H_2O_{(l)}$ → ___ $C_2H_{2(g)}$ + ___ $Ca(OH)_{2(s)}$

20. For each of the following word equations or descriptions, write a balanced equation to represent the reaction. Also, identify the type of reaction.

a) Magnesium metal reacts with hydrochloric acid to form magnesium chloride and hydrogen gas.

b) Aluminum metal reacts with iron (III) oxide to form iron metal and aluminum oxide.

c) Calcium hydroxide reacts with sulfuric acid to produce calcium sulfate and water.

d) Elemental sulfur, S_8, reacts with oxygen gas, O_2, to form sulfur trioxide gas.

e) Lead (II) oxide is decomposed into lead metal and oxygen gas.

f) Propane gas, C_3H_8, burns by combining with oxygen gas to produce carbon dioxide gas and water vapour.

Lesson 16   CHEMICAL REACTION RATES

NOTES

Chemical reactions occur at different rates or speeds. Reactions speed up or slow down depending on the following factors:

- catalysts
- concentration of reactants
- reaction temperature
- surface area of reactants

Catalysts

A catalyst will increase the rate of a reaction, but it is not consumed (used up) in the reaction. If platinum is added to the reaction between hydrogen and oxygen at room temperature, the reaction will go ahead. If platinum is not present, the reaction will not go forth.

Reactions requiring catalysts are present in all living and non-living systems. In biological systems (life forms), these catalysts are called enzymes. The vitamins that humans ingest act as catalysts in our cells.

The knowledge of the application and manipulation of catalysts has aided such areas of human development as the petroleum industry and medical science.

There are many catalysts in the human body that affect not only how the body functions but also how the mind works. About one-third of all schizophrenics can be relieved of all disease symptoms by giving them lithium. Lithium helps the normal flow of energy in cells, and if it is not present, the rate slows down. This limits a person's ability to think clearly.

Foods containing certain enzymes help people learn.
They become especially important during stressful circumstances as the body fights the build-up of toxins in cells. Other enzymes prevent cellular damage from occurring.

Concentration of Reactants

The concentration of reactants will also change the rate of a reaction.
If more of the reacting compounds and elements are present, they will bounce off each other more often. This will speed up the reaction.
If reactants are taken away, it will slow down the reaction rate.

Reaction Temperature

The temperature of the reaction will also determine the speed of the reaction. Increasing the temperature will speed up a reaction; decreasing the temperature will slow it down. Using a heating pad or Bunsen burner during an experiment cause the reaction to occur more quickly.

Surface Area

The surface area of the reactants is also a factor in the reaction rate. If the surface area increases, the rate of the reaction will increase. If the reactants are in large chunks, the surface area is too small to allow the reaction to progress quickly. Grinding the chemicals before they are added together will increase the surface area of each particle and will speed up the reaction. Mixing the chemicals with a stirring rod during the reaction will also speed up the reaction. This action continues to break down the particles into smaller particles (increasing the surface area).

The experiment of lighting a bag of white flour on fire is an example of what demonstrates the importance of particle size. The flour will burn slowly if just left alone. If the same flour is blown over a fire, it will flame up quickly. For this reason, large flour mills have to be very careful in how they handle flour.

PRACTICE EXERCISE

1. A substance that acts as a catalyst is

   A) A metal
   C) A binary compound

   B) An enzyme
   D) A non-metal

2. Increasing the temperature of a reaction will

   A) Decrease the rate of the reaction
   C) Increase the surface area of the reactants

   B) Decrease the surface area of the reactants
   D) Increase the rate of the reaction

3. What happens to the rate of a reaction when the surface area of the reactants is increased?

Lesson 17   MOLES

The atomic mass of each element varies, but the number of atoms does not. This number, known as Avogadro's number, is 6.023×10^{23}. For the sake of convenience, this is called one mole. A mole always contains 6.023×10^{23} items.

To understand how large a mole is, consider the following problem. If a machine can count 10 marbles per second, how many years will it take the machine to count 1 mol of marbles?

$$\frac{6.023 \times 10^{23} \text{ marbles}}{10 \text{ marbles/s}} = 6.023 \times 10^{22} \text{ s}$$

Calculating the number of seconds in a year:
(60 s/min) (60 min/h) (24 h/day) (365 days/year) $= 3.15 \times 10^{7}$ s/year

$$\frac{6.023 \times 10^{22} \text{ s}}{3.15 \times 10^{7} \text{ s/year}} = 1.91 \times 10^{15} \text{ years}$$

This problem shows that the number of items in a mole is extremely large. For this reason, mass is used to measure moles of elements. A mole of an element is represented by its molar mass. For example, the molar mass of $H_2O_{(l)}$ is calculated by adding the atomic molar mass of each element in the compound.

Water ($H_2O_{(l)}$) is made up of two atoms of hydrogen and one atom of oxygen. One mole of water has two moles of hydrogen atoms and one mole of oxygen atoms.

According to the Periodic Table, one mole of hydrogen has a mass of 1.01 g and one mole of oxygen has a mass of 16.00 g.

$$2 \text{ mol H} \times 1.01 \text{ g/mol} = 2.02 \text{ g}$$
$$1 \text{ mol O} \times 16.00 \text{ g/mol} = \underline{16.00 \text{ g}}$$

$$1 \text{ mol of } H_2O = 18.02 \text{ g}$$

The symbol for a mole is mol.

A mole always contains 6.02×10^{23}.

The molar mass of each element is its atomic mass.

- Na — 22.99 g/mol
- O — 16.00 g/mol
- H — 1.01 g/mol

NOTES

For a compound, the molar mass is the sum of all the moles of each element represented in the formula of the compound. For example, the molar mass of sucrose, $C_{12}H_{22}O_{11}$, is calculated as shown below.

Each mole of sucrose consists of 12 moles of carbon (C) atoms, 22 moles of hydrogen (H) atoms, and 11 moles of oxygen (O) atoms.

$$12 \text{ mol C} \times 12.01 \text{ g/mol} = 144.12 \text{ g}$$
$$22 \text{ mol H} \times 1.01 \text{ g/mol} = 22.22 \text{ g}$$
$$11 \text{ mol O} \times 16 \text{ g/mol} = \underline{176.00 \text{ g}}$$

$$1 \text{ mol of } C_{12}H_{22}O_{11} = 342.34 \text{ g}$$

In a balanced equation for a chemical reaction, the coefficients represent the number of moles that are required or produced in the reaction. For example
$$2H_{2(g)} + O_{2(g)} \rightarrow 2H_2O_{(l)}$$
2 mol of $H_{2(g)}$ added to 1 mol of $O_{2(g)}$ makes 2 mol of $H_2O_{(l)}$

NOTE: In a chemical reaction, the mass of the reactants must equal the mass of the products, but the number of moles of the reactants do not have to equal the number of moles of the products.

A mole is equal to
- the molar mass of an element
- 6.023×10^{23} (Avogadro's number)

Moles are represented in an equation by the lower case letter "*n*" and can be determined using the formula:

$$n = \frac{m}{M}$$

where n = number of moles
m = mass
M = molar mass

For example, to find the number of moles of H_2SO_4 in a 100.0 g sample, divide the mass by the molar mass.

$H_2 = 1.01 \times 1 = 2.02$

$S = 32.06 = 32.06$

$O_4 = 16 \times 4 = \underline{64.00}$

$= 98.08$

$$n = \frac{m}{M}$$

$$= \frac{100.0 \text{ g}}{98.08}$$

$$= 1.01 \text{ mol}$$

Molar Mass is the actual mass of 1 mole of a substance. It is the sum of the atomic molar masses of all elements in a compound.

PRACTICE EXERCISE

1. Calculate the molar mass of each of the following compounds.

Formula	Name	Molar Mass (g/mol)
$Na_2SO_{4(s)}$	sodium sulfate	Na $-$ 22.99 $\times$ 2 $=$ 45.98 S $-$ 32.06 $\times$ 1 $=$ 32.06 O $-$ 16.00 $\times$ 4 $=$ <u>64.00</u> molar mass $=$ 142.04
$Ca(NO_3)_{2(s)}$		
$N_2O_{5(g)}$		
$K_2Cr_2O_{7(s)}$		
$Al_2O_{3(s)}$		
$(NH_4)_2SO_{4(s)}$		
$H_2O_{(l)}$		
$NaCl_{(s)}$		

76

2. Fill in the blanks of the following table.

Compound	Number of Atoms or Molecules	Number of Moles	Mass (g)
$NaCl_{(s)}$	6.02×10^{25}	$\dfrac{6.02 \times 10^{25}}{6.02 \times 10^{23}} = 100$	5 844 g or 5.84×10^3 g
$AgNO_{3(s)}$		0.650	
$K_{(s)}$	1.50×10^{23}		
$Zn_{(s)}$			200 g
$Cl_{2(g)}$		3.20	
$NaOH_{(aq)}$			60.0 g
$HCl_{(g)}$	1.20×10^{25}		
$H_2O_{(l)}$			25.0 g
$C_4H_{10(g)}$		2.80	

3. One mole is the equivalent of how many atoms? _____

4. Determine the molar mass of the following compounds.

   a) $H_{2(s)}$

   b) $CH_3OH_{(l)}$

   c) $CoCl_{2(s)}$

5. Using the formula $n = m/M$, find the number of moles in 10.0 g of each compound from question 4.

   a)

   b)

   c)

6. What is the mass, in grams, of 1.50 moles of $H_2O_{(l)}$?

Lesson 18   WHMIS AND MSDS

WHMIS: Workplace Hazardous Material Information System

WHMIS was designed to help people recognize dangers in workplaces.
Each danger was given a specific symbol.

There are eight standard symbols that have been designed to advise people
that they must be careful in handling materials.

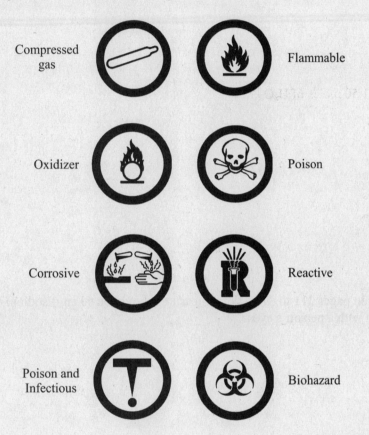

Compressed gas

Flammable

Oxidizer

Poison

Corrosive

Reactive

Poison and Infectious

Biohazard

MSDS: Material Safety Data Sheet

In Canada, all chemicals must have an attached data sheet that identifies
the chemical and physical properties and dangers of the chemical.
In addition to the appropriate WHMIS symbol, each sheet gives the
melting point, boiling point and toxicity of the material, and first aid, spill,
and clean-up procedures.

PRACTICE EXERCISE

1. What do the following WHMIS symbols indicate?

    a)

    b)

    c)

    d)

2. Consult the sample MSDS on pages 311 to 312. What measures should be taken if sodium hydroxide comes in contact with a person's eyes?

PRACTICE TEST

1. Fill in the blanks for the following diagrams, and name each.

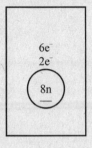

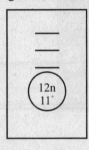

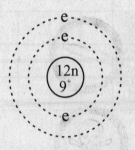

Name _____   Name _____   Name _____

2. Show atom-ion transformation for the following diagrams.

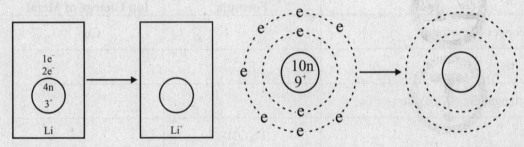

3. Fill in the chart for binary acids and oxyacids.

Acid Name	Formula	Binary Acid /Oxyacid
nitric acid		
	$HCl_{(aq)}$	
hydrofluoric acid		
	$H_2SO_{4(aq)}$	

4. Give the family name for each of the shaded areas on the outline of the Periodic Table below.

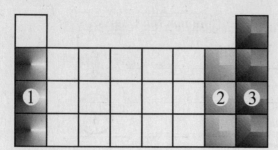

1.

2.

3.

5. Fill in the missing information on the chart below.

Name	Formula	Ion Charge of Metal
copper (II) nitrate		Cu^{2+}
	F_2O_3	
manganese (IV) oxide		
	$Fe(OH)_2$	

6. Fill in the table below.

Isotope Name	Symbol	Number of Electrons	Number of Neutrons	Number of Protons
sodium – 25	$^{25}_{11}Na$			
sodium – 24	$^{24}_{11}Na$			
hydrogen – 1	$^{1}_{1}H$			
hydrogen – 2	$^{2}_{1}H$			

7. Fill in the table below.

Name	Atomic Symbol	Common Ion Charge
Nitrogen		
Lithium		
	Na	
Oxygen		
	F	
	S	
Magnesium		

8. Suggest the simplest method of separating the parts of a suspension.

9. Complete the following chart.

Element	Atomic Number	Number of Protons	Number of Neutrons	Number of Electrons	Atomic Mass
He					
C					
Na					
Cu					

10. One method of separating alcohol from water is to

A) extract it   B) distill it
C) filter it   D) chromatograph it

11. Name three characteristics of metals.

-

-

-

12. For each of the following chemical reactions, identify the reaction type and balance the equation.

Type:

a) ____   ____ $MgS_{(s)} \rightarrow$ ___ $Mg_{(s)} +$ ___ $S_{8(s)}$

b) ____   ____ $Ca(NO_3)_{2(aq)} +$ ___ $Na_{(s)} \rightarrow$ ___ $NaNO_{3(aq)} +$ ___ $Ca_{(s)}$

c) ____   ____ $C_5H_{12(g)} +$ ___ $O_{2(g)} \rightarrow$ ___ $CO_{2(g)} +$ ___ $H_2O_{(l)}$

13. Write the word equation for each of the following balanced equations and write what type of reaction it is.

Type:

a) ____ $H_2SO_{4(aq)} + 2NaOH_{(aq)} \rightarrow 2H_2O_{(l)} + Na_2SO_{4(aq)}$

b) ____ $Cu_{(s)} + 2AgNO_{3(aq)} \rightarrow Cu(NO_3)_{2(aq)} + 2Ag_{(s)}$

c) ____ $CH_{4(g)} + 2O_{2(g)} \rightarrow CO_{2(g)} + 2H_2O_{(g)}$

14. Match.

a) $CO_{2(aq)}$ ____   **1.** acid

b) $Ne_{(g)}$ ____   **2.** molecular compound

c) $NaCl_{(s)}$ ____   **3.** noble gas

d) $HCO_{3(aq)}$ ____   **4.** halogen

e) $Cl_{2(aq)}$ ____   **5.** ionic compound

15. Consider the balanced equation.

$P_{4(s)} + 5O_{2(g)} \rightarrow 2P_2O_{5(g)}$

a) What is the number of moles of $O_{2(g)}$ represented in this reaction?

b) What is the total number of moles of both reactants?

c) What is the total number of moles of product?

d) Compare the total moles of reactants with the total moles of product?

16. Complete the following chart.

Compound	Formula	Molar Mass	Moles	Mass
Water			2.0	
Methanol			1.5	
	$NaNO_3$			100 g
	$Ca(OH)_2$		1.0	
Sodium carbonate				10 g

17. Match each of the following WHMIS symbols to its meaning.

1.

a)   Compressed gas ____

b)   Poison   ____

c)   Reactive   ____

d)   Biohazard   ____ ____

2.

3.

4.

ENERGY FLOW IN TECHNOLOGICAL SYSTEMS

When you are finished this unit, you will be able to…

- use examples to illustrate the forms of energy and the natural and technological systems used to transform energy from one form to another
- define kinetic, potential, mechanical, thermal, and chemical energy in relation to one another
- apply the concepts of scalar and vector quantities to describe displacement, velocity, acceleration, momentum, and inertia
- relate gravitational potential energy to the concepts of work and force
- measure quantities of energy using graphical and algebraic techniques
- apply the principles of energy conservation and thermodynamics to describe and predict the efficiency of energy transformations in technological systems
- explain the costs, benefits, efficiency, and sustainability of energy sources using thermodynamic principles

Lesson	Page	Completed On
1. Motion	88	
2. Graphical Determination of Velocity	94	
3. Acceleration	107	
4. Acceleration Due to Gravity	115	
5. Force	117	
6. Work	120	
7. Power	124	
8. Kinetic Energy (E_k)	127	
9. Potential Energy (E_p)	131	
10. Mechanical Energy ($E_k + E_p$)	135	
11. Thermodynamics	141	
12. Heat Engines	147	
Practice Test	151	

PREREQUISITE SKILLS AND KNOWLEDGE

Prior to starting this unit, you should be able to…
- describe heat energy needs and technologies, thermal energy, heat transfer and energy conservation
- apply the concepts of force and motion to mechanical systems
- identify the forms of energy and the principles of energy transformation
- solve equations using fractions and exponents
- define variables to create and interpret scatter plots, using lines of best fit

Lesson 1   MOTION

NOTES

Motion is the change in position of an object. The object's position can change in one or more directions.

Uniform motion is a constant rate of change. If the speed of a car remains steady at 50 km/h, then the car is travelling at a uniform speed.

Displacement (d) – change in position
Velocity (v) – rate of change in position
Acceleration (a) – rate of change in velocity

We measure motion in terms of
- displacement or distance (d) – the change in position of the object

- velocity or speed (v) – the rate of change in an object's position

- acceleration (a) – the rate of change in an object's velocity

Displacement (d)

Displacement
– vector quantity
– includes direction
– includes magnitude
  (distance)

Displacement is a vector quantity, which means that it includes both direction and magnitude.

Displacement refers to how far a person or object has moved, regardless of the length of the path taken during the move. Because displacement is concerned with the difference between start point and has a directional value from the starting point. Think of displacement as the measurement of the shortest path connecting two points.

Distance
– scalar quantity

For example, the displacement of a ball thrown upward could be *3.0 m upward* or a person could move from one position to another such that his displacement is *5.0 m east*.

Distance (d)

Distance is a scale quantity, which means that it contains only magnitude. Distance refers to how far a person or object travels, regardless of direction. Think of distance as the measurement of the actual path connecting two points.

If a person walks from her house around the block and then back to her house, her displacement is zero. She is right back to her starting point. However the distance she walked is 4.0 blocks.

Speed (v)

Speed tells us how fast an object is travelling, but it does not refer to the direction of travel.

$$speed = \frac{distance}{time}$$

For example, a car that travels 60 km in 1 h has a speed of *60 km/h*.

Velocity (v)

Velocity is a speed in a defined direction. It can be determined with a simple formula that relates distance to time, namely:

$$v = \frac{displacement}{time} = \frac{change\ in\ distance}{change\ in\ time} = \frac{\Delta d}{\Delta t}$$

For example, a car that travels north for 1 h and that travels 110 km in that time has a velocity of *110 km/h north*.

Average Velocity

Average velocity is a measure of motion over an extended period of time.

$$v_{(average)} = \frac{Distance_{(final)} - Distance_{(initial)}}{Time_{(final)} - Time_{(initial)}}$$

$$v_a = \frac{d_f - d_i}{t_f - t_i} = \frac{total\ distance\ travelled}{total\ time\ taken} = \frac{\Delta d}{\Delta t}$$

Example 1

A car travels 35 km in 0.50 h. Determine its speed.

Solution

$$speed = \frac{distance}{time}$$
$$= \frac{35\ km}{0.05\ h}$$
$$= 70\ km/h$$

Speed
– scalar quantity
Is the rate of change

Velocity
– vector quantity
– is speed in a definite direction

$$v = \frac{\Delta d}{\Delta t}$$

Δ – Greek letter meaning change

Average velocity:

$$v_a = \frac{d_f - d_i}{t_f - t_i}$$

Example 2

Bronwyn walks 250 m east and then turns around and walks 300 m west. The whole trip takes 300 s.

a) What is the total distance that Brownyn travelled?

Solution

Total distance $= 250 \text{ m} + 300$
$= 550 \text{ m}$

b) What was Brownyn's displacement?

Solution

Total displacement $= 300 \text{ m west} - 250 \text{ m east}$
$= 50 \text{ m west}$

The 250 was the negative because it is in the opposite direction.

c) What was Bronwyn's average speed for the whole trip?

Solution

$$\text{Average speed} = \frac{\text{Total distance}}{\text{Total time}}$$
$$= \frac{550 \text{ m}}{300 \text{ s}}$$
$$= 1.83 \text{ m/s}$$

d) What was Bronwyn's average velocity for the whole trip?

Solution

$$\text{Average velocity} = \frac{\text{Total displacement}}{\text{Total time}}$$
$$= \frac{50 \text{ m west}}{300 \text{ s}}$$
$$= 0.17 \text{ m/s west}$$

PRACTICE EXERCISE

1. A boy rides his bike once around a city block, as illustrated below.

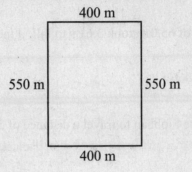

400 m

550 m   550 m

400 m

   a) What distance did the boy travel?

   b) What was the boy's displacement after he completed the ride?

2. An object travels 30 m north and then turns around and travels 12 m south. The total time of travel is 9.0 s.

   a) What is the object's average speed?

   b) What is the object's average velocity?

3. An object is travelling at a constant velocity of 15 m/s north. How far will it travel in 5.0 s?

   A) 15 m   B) 45 m
   C) 75 m   D) 95 m

4. A cyclist rode at 5.6 m/s for 20 min. What distance did she travel?

5. Calculate the average speed in meters per second of a boat that travelled 8.0 km in 0.6 h.

6. A ball is dropped from a height of 65.0 m took 3.61 s to fall. Find the average velocity of the ball.

7. How many seconds would it take Siobhan to travel a distance of 5 000 m if she ran at an average speed of 2.5 m/s?

8. A car travelled 1.0×10^3 km in 25 h. Find the car's average speed in kilometres per hour..

9. Meredith runs at an average velocity of 1.3 m/s north for 90 s. She then walks at an average velocity of 0.5 m/s south for 90 s.

   a) What is the total distance she travelled?

   b) What was her average speed for the entire trip?

   c) How far is she from her start point?

   d) What was her average velocity for the entire trip?

10. To travel from her small town to a city 700 km away, Alicia left at 6:00 AM and arrived at 8:30 PM. What was her average speed?

A) 1.34 m/s   **B)** 13.4 m/s

C) 134 m/s   **D)** 1 340 m/s

11. A roller skater made a complete circle with a radius of 8.50 m in 12.0 s.

a) What was his average speed?

b) What was his average velocity?

Lesson 2   *GRAPHICAL DETERMINATION OF VELOCITY*

Velocity can be determined by plotting a set of data for distance and time on a graph.

To learn how to do this, imagine that car starts moving forward from a stop sign. The distance that it travels is recorded every second for six seconds, are shown below.

time (s)	distance (m)
0	0
1	2
2	4
3	8
4	12
5	20
6	28

- The first step in setting up a graph is to consider what values to use for each axis and to determine the scale.

  $t = 0$ to 6 s
  $d = 0$ to 28 m

- Often graphs are scaled by 1, 2, 5, 10, 20, or 50 values.
  It is important that the scale values used are appropriate for the data.

- Time is always plotted on the horizontal axis.

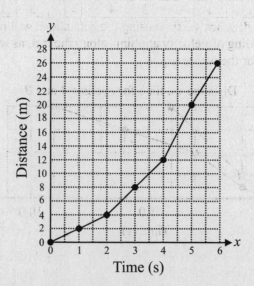

- When the graph is completed, identify all the straight segments formed. In this example, there are three straight segments;
- – time 0 to 2 s
- – time 2 to 4 s
- – time 4 to 6 s
- Next, determine the speed for each straight segment.

- – time 0 s to 2 s:
  Total distance travelled = 4 m
  $$\therefore v = \frac{\Delta d}{\Delta t} = \frac{4 \text{ m}}{2 \text{ s}} = 2 \text{ m/s}$$

- – time 2 s to 4 s:
  Total distance travelled = 12 m – 4 m = 8 m
  $$\therefore v = \frac{\Delta d}{\Delta t} = \frac{8 \text{ m}}{2 \text{ s}} = 4 \text{ m/s}$$

- – time 4 s to 6 s:
  Total distance travelled = 28 m – 12 m = 16 m
  $$\therefore v = \frac{\Delta d}{\Delta t} = \frac{16 \text{ m}}{2 \text{ s}} = 8 \text{ m/s}$$

In this example, the velocity of the car from 0 s to 2 s was 2 m/s; from 2 s to 4 s; it was 4 m/s; and, from 4 s to 6 s, it was 8 m/s.

Cyclist A and cyclist B travelled the following distances in the times shown.

Cyclist A					Cyclist B			
Distance (m)	10	20	30	40	5	20	30	40
Time (s)	1	2	3	4	1	3	6	9

- Graphing distance vs. time using the data above will result in a clear understanding of velocity at points along the trip, as well as the velocity for the whole trip.

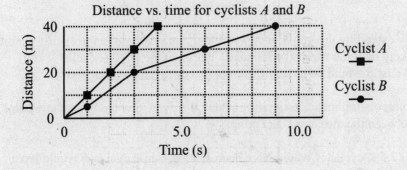

NOTES

- The graph for cyclist A's is a single straight line, which indicates that she travelled at a constant speed. The graph for cyclist B can be broken into two straight lines, from 0 s to 3 s and from 3 s to 9 s.

- Cyclist A average speed

$$v = \frac{\Delta d}{\Delta t} = \frac{40\text{ m} - 0\text{ m}}{4.0\text{ s} - 0\text{ s}} = 10\text{ m/s}$$

- Cyclist B average speed
  0 s to 3 s segment

$$v = \frac{\Delta d}{\Delta t} = \frac{20\text{ m} - 0\text{ m}}{3.0\text{ s} - 0\text{ s}} = 6.7\text{ m/s}$$

  3 s to 9 s segment

$$v = \frac{\Delta d}{\Delta t} = \frac{40\text{ m} - 20\text{ m}}{9.0\text{ s} - 3.0\text{ s}} = \frac{20\text{ m}}{6.0\text{ s}} = 3.3\text{ m/s}$$

It is also possible to find distances not explicitly given in data by extrapolating and interpolating points.

**Extrapolation –
devising information
beyond the data in the
graph**

Extrapolating means using the graph to estimate where the cyclist would be at a specific time not measured by these data.

Distance vs. time for cyclists A and B

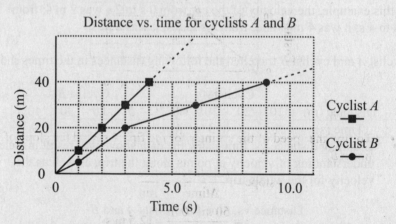

By extending the graph, it is possible to measure where the cyclist would likely be if the trip had continued. For example at 10 s, cyclist A and cyclist B would be at very different places as can be seen above.

**Interpolation –
devising information from
within the measured data**

Interpolating means estimating where the cyclist would be at some point between the measured data points.

At 2.5 s, cyclist A would have been at 27 m while cyclist B would have been at 17.5 m.

Interpolation makes it possible to determine where change happens between measured periods. Knowing where a change occurs allows the diagnosis of problems. The data in the graph may indicate that cyclist *B* is not able to cycle at a consistent pace. With a little training, the performance graph of *B* may look like the performance graph of *A*.

Slope

The slope of any line is equal to the change in the vertical direction divided by the change in the horizontal direction.

Determining the slope between two points on a distance–time graph is done by finding the vertical difference between the two points and dividing it by the horizontal difference between the two points.

$$\text{slope} = \frac{\Delta \text{ distance}}{\Delta \text{ time}} = \frac{\text{rise}}{\text{run}}$$

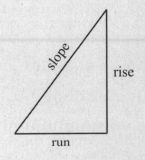

$$\text{slope} = \frac{\text{rise}}{\text{run}}$$

In the example below, the graph shows the motion of a world–class sprinter.

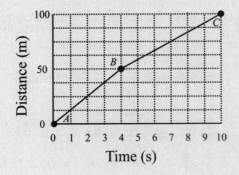

- To find the speed of the sprinter for the first 4 s, find the slope of line *AB*.

$$\text{slope} = \frac{\Delta \text{distance}}{\Delta \text{time}} = \frac{\text{rise}}{\text{run}}$$

$$= \frac{50 \text{ m} - 0 \text{ m}}{4 \text{ s} - 0 \text{ s}} = 12.5 \text{ m/s}$$

- To find the sprinter's speed for the last 6 s, find the slope of line *BC*.

$$\text{slope} = \frac{\Delta \text{distance}}{\Delta \text{time}} = \frac{\text{rise}}{\text{run}}$$

$$= \frac{100 \text{ m} - 50 \text{ m}}{10 \text{ s} - 4 \text{ s}} = \frac{50 \text{ m}}{6 \text{ s}} = 8.3 \text{ m/s}$$

In another example, the acceleration of a bicycle and the acceleration of a car are shown on the distance–time graph below.

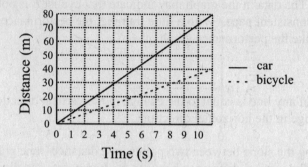

- To calculate the distance travelled by each vehicle at a certain time, read directly from the graph.

    e.g.,   at 4 s,
    – bicycle is at 13 m
    – car is at 30 m

The average speed is valid for any point on a *straight* line segment.

- Find the average speed for the bicycle and the car respectively, after 8.0 s of travel.

$$\text{bicycle}: \quad v = \frac{\Delta d}{\Delta t} = \frac{29 \text{ m}}{8 \text{ s}} = 3.6 \text{ m/s}$$

$$\text{car}: \qquad v = \frac{\Delta d}{\Delta t} = \frac{58 \text{ m}}{8 \text{ s}} = 7.3 \text{ m/s}$$

Graphical Determination of Distance

The following is a velocity–time graph.

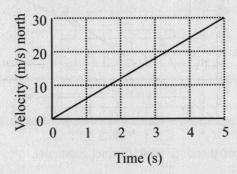

To find the distance travelled on the above graph, find the area under the line.

To find the displacement after 5.0 s, draw the vertical line from 5.0 s until it intersects the graph line, and shade in the area back to the starting point. The shaded area gives a triangle for which the area must be found.

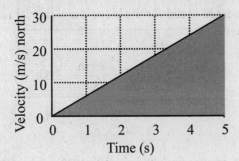

$$A = \frac{1}{2}bh \; (b = \text{base}, \, h = \text{height})$$

$$= \frac{1}{2}(5.0 \text{ m})(30 \text{ m/s})$$

$$= 75 \text{ m north}$$

The area under the graph gives the distance (displacement) of travel.

The following is a velocity–time graph.

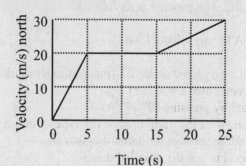

- On the graph, there are three distinct segments.
  0–5 s,
  5–15 s, and
  15–25 s

- To calculate the distance travelled in each segment, find the area of each segment.

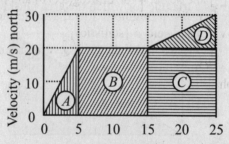

- Segment A: triangle: $\frac{1}{2}bh = \frac{1}{2}(5.0 \text{ s})(20 \text{ m/s}) = 50 \text{ m}$

  Segment B: rectangle: $bh = (10 \text{ s}) (20 \text{ m/s}) = 200 \text{ m}$
  Segment C: rectangle: $bh = (10 \text{ s}) (20 \text{ m/s}) = 200 \text{ m}$

  Segment D: triangle: $\frac{1}{2}bh = \frac{1}{2}(10 \text{ s})(10 \text{ m/s}) = 50 \text{ m}$

- Calculate the total displacement for the whole trip by adding the displacements for all four segments.
  50 m + 200 m + 200 m + 50 m = 500 m south

- Find the average velocity for the entire trip by finding the total displacement divided by the total time.

$$v_a = \frac{\Delta d}{\Delta t} = \frac{500 \text{ m}}{25 \text{ s}} = 20 \text{ m/s south}$$

A graphing calculator can be used to perform these calculations and produce this graph? The process is as follows:

- Press: [STAT] and select [1:Edit].
-
- Enter the list you have under L1 (put a number in, then press [Enter] each time you enter a number).
- Plot the data by pressing [2nd] [Y=].
- Press [Enter] for Plot 1 and choose the type of graph wanted.
- Set the window settings to match the data size.
- Press [Graph] to see the graphed data.

A graphing calculator will also give you a line of best fit, linear regression, standard deviation, etc.

For the TI-83/Plus calculator, use the procedure below.
- Find the Catalogue menu.
- Press [2nd] 0 and select diagnostics ON and [enter].
- Press [stat] [>] and select 4 for LinReg(ax+b) and press [enter].
- To graph the line if you originally found a scatterplot, then press[Y=] [Vars] and selct 5 [statistics].
- Then press [>] twice to highlight the EQ variables menu.
- Press 1: [RegEQ].
- Press [Graph].

Example 1

The following data was recorded for a car.

Distance (km)	0	600	1200
Time (h)	0	10	20

a) Draw a graph showing the car's travel.

Solution

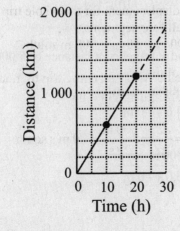

Distance vs. time for a car

b) What is the velocity of the car at 5.0 h and 20 h of travel?

Solution

$$\text{At } 5 \text{ h} \quad v = \frac{\Delta d}{\Delta t} = \frac{300 \text{ km}}{5.0 \text{ h}}$$

$$= 60 \text{ km/h}$$

$$\text{At } 20 \text{ h} \quad v = \frac{\Delta d}{\Delta t} = \frac{1\,200 \text{ km}}{20 \text{ h}}$$

$$= 60 \text{ km/h}$$

c) Extrapolate what distance the car would travel in 30 h?

Solution

The dotted line gives the extrapolation value; at 30 h, the distance is 1 800 km.

Example 2

Given the graph below, find the average velocity of bullets *A* and *B* that were fired from the same gun.

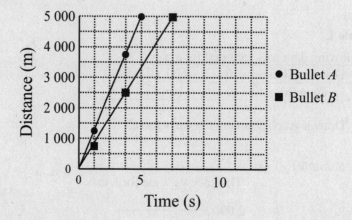

Solution

Both bullets *A* and *B* travelled a distance of 5 000 m, but in different lengths of time.

$$v_a = \frac{d_f - d_i}{t_f - t_i} = \frac{5\,000 \text{ m} - 0 \text{ m}}{4.0 \text{ s} - 0 \text{ m}}$$

$$= 1\,250 \text{ m/s}$$

$$v_b = \frac{d_f - d_i}{t_f - t_i} = \frac{5\,000 \text{ m} - 0 \text{ m}}{6.0 \text{ s} - 0 \text{ m}}$$

$$= 833 \text{ m/s}$$

$$= 8.3 \times 10^2 \text{ m/s}$$

Alternate Solution

The slope of a distance-time graph gives the velocity.

Slope of bullet A = $= 1\,250$ m/s
                          $= 1.3 \times 10^3$ m/s

5 000 m

4.0 s

Slope of bullet B = $= 833$ m/s
                          $= 8.3 \times 10^2$ m/s

5 000 m

6.0 s

PRACTICE EXERCISE

1. The following data is for an object travelling south.

Distance (m)	0	4	8	8	8	10	12	20	28
Time (s)	0	2	4	6	8	10	12	14	16

a) Using the data above, plot the displacement–time graph on the grid below.

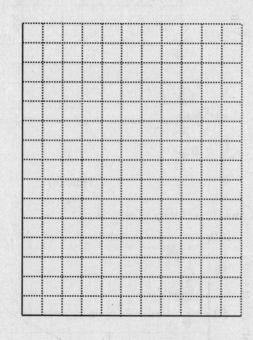

Time (s)

b) From the graph above and the slopes of each segment, plot the velocity–time graph of the object on the grid below.

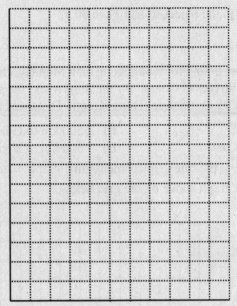

Time (s)

2. The following graph shows the velocity of an object.

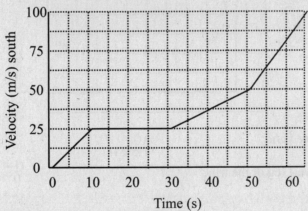

Time (s)

a) What is the object's velocity at 10 s?

b) What is the displacement of the object from 10 s to 30 s?

c) What is the average velocity from 50 s to 65 s?

d) What is the displacement of the object from 30 s to 50 s?

e) What is happening to the object from 10 s to 30 s?

3. A ship leaves Vancouver bound for Hong Kong on a Monday. In one week, it travels to Hawaii. By the second week, it arrives in Guam. By the third week, the ship is in Tokyo, and at the end of the four weeks, it arrives at its destination (Hong Kong). Distances travelled are listed below:

A) 4 000 km to Hawaii   **B)** 3 500 km to Guam
C) 2 500 km to Tokyo, and   **D)** 3 500 km to Hong Kong

A) Plot the data on the graph above on the grid below.

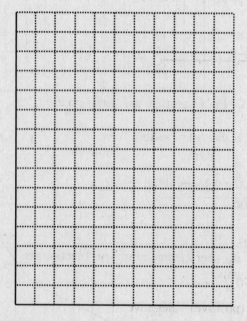

Hint: Use weeks as the time value.

b) What was the slowest leg of the trip?

c) What was the fastest leg of the trip?

d) What was the average speed for the whole trip?

Lesson 3   ACCELERATION

Acceleration is a measure of the change in velocity divided by the change in time.

Acceleration: $a = \dfrac{\Delta v}{\Delta t}$

Because acceleration is a change in velocity divided by time, acceleration is a vector quantity.

$a = \dfrac{\Delta v}{\Delta t}$

Uniform Acceleration

Positive acceleration

- Acceleration is positive if both magnitude and direction are positive.

(positive) (positive) = positive

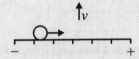

- Acceleration is also positive if both magnitude and direction are negative.

(negative) (negative) = positive

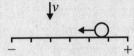

Negative acceleration

- Negative acceleration occurs if either the magnitude or direction are negative while the other is positive.

(negative) (positive) = negative

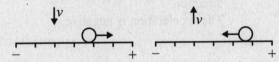

NOTES

$$a_{(average)} = \frac{v_f - v_i}{d_f - d_i}$$

Uniform acceleration can be found using the formula:

$$a_{(average)} = \frac{v_{(final)} - v_{(initial)}}{t_{(final)} - t_{(initial)}} = \frac{v_f - v_i}{t_f - v_i}$$

The units of measure for acceleration are meters per second squared: m/s^2.

Where velocity remains constant over time, a velocity–time graph would look like this:

No change in velocity
$$\therefore a = 0$$

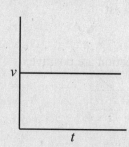

Since there is no change in velocity, the acceleration is zero.

Where velocity is increasing at a constant rate, a velocity–time graph would look like this:

Velocity is increasing
$$\therefore a = +$$

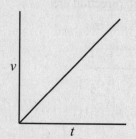

The velocity is increasing in a positive direction.
The acceleration is positive.

Where velocity is decreasing at a constant rate, a velocity–time graph would look like this:

Velocity is decreasing
$$\therefore a = -$$

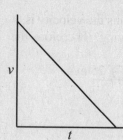

The velocity is changing in a negative direction.
The acceleration is negative.

108

Acceleration can be calculated either mathematically or by using a velocity–time graph, as shown below.

The following data is for an object going west (positive).

Velocity(m/s)	0	5	10	15	20	25
Time (s)	0	1	2	3	4	5

- Mathematically:

$$a = \frac{v_f - v_i}{t_f - t_i} = \frac{25 \text{ m/s} - 0 \text{ m/s}}{5 \text{ s} - 0 \text{ s}} = 5 \text{ m/s}^2 \text{ west}$$

- Graphically:

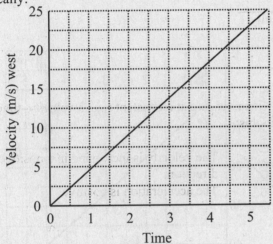

- The slope of the line:

$$\text{slope} = \frac{\text{rise}}{\text{run}} = \frac{25 \text{ m/s}}{5 \text{ s}} = 5 \text{ m/s}^2$$

Notice that in each method, time is squared, which means the velocity is increasing 5 m/s for every second that the object is moving. Therefore, the object moves from

0 m/s → 5 m/s → 10 m/s → 15 m/s → 20 m/s → 25 m/s.

Consider a second example. The following data is for an object that is dropped from a building and falls to the ground.

Velocity (m/s)	0	−10	−20	−30	−40
Time (s)	0	1	2	3	4

• Mathematically:

$$a = \frac{v_f - v_i}{t_f - t_i} = \frac{-40 \text{ m/s}}{4.0 \text{ s}} = 10 \text{ m/s}^2 \text{ down, which is negative}$$

$$\therefore a = -10 \text{ m/s}^2$$

• Graphically:

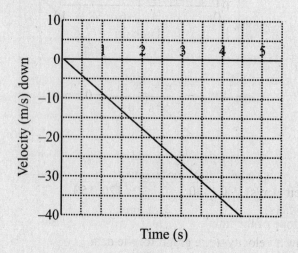

Time (s)

$$\text{slope} = \frac{\text{rise}}{\text{run}} = \frac{-40 \text{ m/s}}{4.0 \text{ s}} = -10 \text{ m/s}^2$$

Example 1

The following is velocity–time graph showing the motion of a car.
Determine the acceleration of the car.

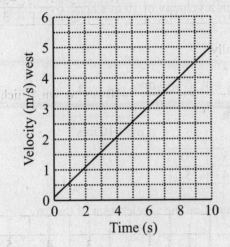

Solution

$$a = \frac{v_f - v_i}{t_f - t_i} = \frac{5 \text{ m/s} - 0 \text{ m/s}}{10 \text{ s} - 0 \text{ s}} = 0.5 \text{ m/s}^2$$

Example 2

The data below is for an object moving west.

Velocity (m/s)	0	30	60	90	120	150
Time(s)	0	1	2	3	4	5

a) Draw a velocity–time graph for the data.

Solution

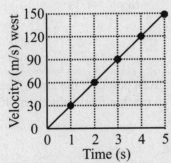

b) Determine the acceleration of the object.

Solution

$$a = \frac{v_f - v_i}{t_f - t_i} = \frac{150 \text{ m/s} - 0 \text{ m/s}}{5 \text{ s} - 0 \text{ s}} = 30 \text{ m/s}^2 \text{ west}$$

PRACTICE EXERCISE

1. What is a runner's acceleration when he attains a velocity of 10 m/s north over 2.5 s?

2. The following data is for a car travelling south.

Velocity (m/s)	0	2	4	6	8	10
Time (s)	0	1	2	3	4	5

   On the grid below, graph the above data and find the acceleration of the car.

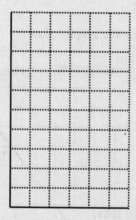

3. The acceleration of a car is 5.0 m/s². The initial velocity of the car was 20.0 m/s over 3.0 . Determine the car's final velocity.

4. The initial velocity of an aircraft is 100 m/s over a given point. If the aircraft accelerates at the rate of 50 m/s², determine the time it will take the aircraft to reach a final velocity of 400 m/s.

5. If a vehicle accelerates at 3.8 m/s² and its initial velocity was 50 km/h, how long , should it take to reach a speed of 100 km/h. (Hint: Remember 1 000 m = 1 km and 3 600 s = an hour.)

6. If a sprinter accelerates from rest at 5.2 m/s^2 for 2.0 s, what is his final speed?

7. If a car has an initial speed of 120 km/h and slows down to 50.0 km/h at a rate of –11.2 m/s^2, how long will it take to slow down?

A) 1.7 s   **B)** 3.5 s
C) 6.6 s   **D)** 10.3 s

8. Terry has an old Chevy that accelerates at a rate of 3.8 m/s^2. How much time would it take Terry to reach the speed limit of 110 km/h if she was already travelling at 70.0 km/h?

A) 2.9 s   **B)** 3.7 s
C) 5.4 s   **D)** 30.0 s

9. Find the acceleration of a boat based on the graph below.

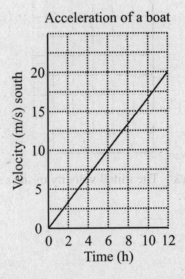

10. The brakes are applied to a car travelling at 25 m/s. The time taken to stop the car is 5.0 s. What is the car's acceleration? (Hint: slowing down is negative)

11. Determine the time a rocket would take to accelerate from 0 m/s to a velocity of 1 000 m/s if its acceleration were 30.0 m/s^2.

12. Find the acceleration of an aircraft that begins its take off from standing still at the end of the runway and has its lift-off at 220 km/h: The time it takes is 20.0 s.

13. Find the acceleration of a skier sliding down a mountain at a rate of 32.0 m/s for 10.0 s.

14. Determine what type of acceleration is shown in each of these graphs.

Type

a)

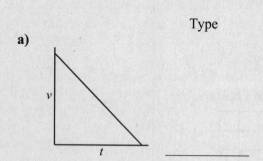

_____

b)

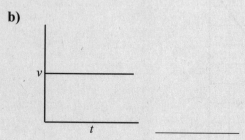

_____

c)

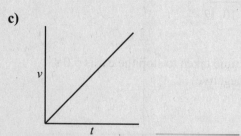

_____

Lesson 4   *ACCELERATION DUE TO GRAVITY*

Sir Isaac Newton, among others, determined that the acceleration due to the pull of Earth's gravity is 9.81 m/s^2. This is called the gravitational constant. An object in free fall is limited to this acceleration.

What this means is that gravity pulls at a constant rate. Because of this constant rate, it is possible to determine how fast something will fall and the time it takes to fall a certain distance.

The formula $a = \dfrac{v_f - v_i}{t}$, where V_p is final velocity, V_i is velocity, and t is

time can be rearranged so that any of these variables can be determined.

v_f, v_i, and t can be determined by rearranging the formula.

A ball falling from a building has an initial velocity of 5.0 m/s and takes 5.0 s to reach the ground. Determine the ball's final velocity.

$$a = \frac{v_f - v_i}{t}$$

$$v_f = v_i + at$$

$$= 5.0 \text{ m/s} + \left(9.81 \text{ m/s}^2\right)\left(5.0 \text{ s}\right)$$

$$= 54 \text{ m/s}$$

PRACTICE EXERCISE

1. A plant falls from a balcony and takes 3.0 s to reach the ground. At what velocity does the plant hit the ground?

2. Find the acceleration of an object if the final velocity is 400 m/s, the initial velocity is 25.0 m/s, and the time taken to change velocity is 25.0 s.

3. If a toy falls off a balcony and its final speed before impact with the ground is 17.5 m/s, then the time it took to hit the ground is

   A) 1.78 s   **B)** 3.25 s
   C) 6.75 s   **D)** 12.0 s

4. The velocity of a skydiver after 5.02 s of free fall is

   A) 12.4 m/s   **B)** 49.2 m/s
   C) 54.6 m/s   **D)** 110 m/s

5. A rock is thrown straight down off a cliff. The release velocity is 5.0 m/s, and the rock hits the ground with a velocity of 14 m/s. Find the time it took the rock to fall.

6. On Planet Z, a rock is dropped and takes 4.0 s to hit the ground at 24 m/s. What is the gravitational acceleration on this planet?

7. Find the velocity in m/s of a skydiver after 6.0 s of free fall. What would this velocity be in kilometres per hour?

Lesson 5 FORCE

Force is an actual influence brought to bear on an object that causes it to move. Force is either a push or a pull. The unit of measurement of force (F) is a newton (N), named after Sir Isaac Newton.

A Newton is the measure of $1 \text{ kg} \times \text{m/s}^2$.

If an object is pushed and it moves, a force has been exerted on it. If the object does not move, no force has been exerted. Do not mistake force for effort.

Measuring force is important in the determination of the amount of energy needed to move an object any distance. For example, to lift a satellite into space, scientists need to know how long the rocket must fire and how much force the engine must create.

Force can be determined by multiplying the mass of an object by its acceleration: $F = ma$
$$N = kg \times m/s^2$$

There is no force exerted if the object does not move or moves at a constant rate.

Force is measured in newtons.

$F = ma$

Example 1

A 500 g object is accelerating at a rate of 0.45 m/s^2. What force is needed to accomplish this?

Solution

Convert 500 g to kg $= 500/1\ 000 = 0.500$ kg
$$\begin{aligned} F &= ma \\ &= (0.500 \text{ kg}) (0.45 \text{ m/s}^2) \\ &= 0.225 \text{ N} \end{aligned}$$

Example 2

A 15 000 kg rocket must reach an acceleration of $8\ 333.3 \text{ m/s}^2$ in order to escape Earth's gravity. What is the force needed to move this rocket into orbit?

Solution

$$\begin{aligned} F &= ma \\ &= (15\ 000 \text{ kg}) (8\ 333.3 \text{ m/s}^2) \\ &= 1.25 \times 10^8 \text{ N} \end{aligned}$$

PRACTICE EXERCISE

1. How much force is needed to accelerate a 15.0 kg object at 5.5 m/s²?

2. If a pencil of 5.0 g is flicked with a force of 8.5 N, what acceleration results?

3. A force of 6.5×10^3 N is exerted on an object resulting in an acceleration of 10.0 m/s².
    What is the mass of the object?

4. Given an 80 kg object with a final velocity of 40 m/s that started from 0.0 m/s just 5.0 s before,
    determine the force needed to move this object.

5. A 1 000 kg car traveling at 25 m/s takes 5.2 s to reach a speed of 30 m/s. Calculate the force exerted
    by the engine that is necessary to change the velocity.

6. Determine the mass of an object if its weight is 80 N near Earth's surface.

    Hint: Use acceleration of gravity

7. **a)** A rocket with a mass of 26 g can cause a force of 20 N. Find the acceleration.

118

b) If the rocket can fire for only 0.8 s, what is the maximum speed of the rocket?

8. A car accelerates from 0 to 110 km/h in 10 s, and it takes 4.5×10^3 N to move the car. What is the mass of the car?

9. A 1 000 kg car travelling at 20 m/s takes 5.0 s to reach a speed of 30 m/s. Find the force needed to move the car.

Lesson 6   WORK

Work is measured in joules (J).

Work is a measure of the transference of energy produced by a motion when a force is applied. If force is applied, the object will move. If it doesn't move force was NOT applied. Work is a measurement of the energy used during the movement. The units of measure for work are joules (J).

Work can be determined by multiplying the force required times the resulting change in distance or displacement.

$$\text{Work} = \text{force} \times \text{displacement}$$

$W = Fd$
Or
$W = mad$

$$W = Fd$$

Since
$$F = \text{mass} \times \text{acceleration}$$
$$= ma$$

then
$$\text{Work} = \text{mass} \times \text{acceleration} \times \text{displacement}$$
$$W = mad$$

where
m = mass (in kg)
a = acceleration (in m/s^2)
d = displacement or distance (in metres)
$F = ma$ (in N)

$$\text{Work} = Fd$$
$$= \text{N} \times \text{m}$$
$$= \text{J}$$

$$\text{Work} = mad$$
$$= (\text{kg})\,(\text{m/s}^2)\,(\text{m})$$
$$= \text{kg} \times \text{m}^2/\text{s}^2$$
$$= \text{J}$$

For work to be done there must be:
- Movement
- a force applied
- the force and displacement must be in the same direction

Remember that there is no work done if nothing moves.

Example 1

Find the work done to push a large container 20 m across a room given that 20 N of force is required.

Solution
$W = Fd$
$\quad = (20\ \text{N})\,(20\ \text{m})$
$\quad = 400\ \text{J}$

Example 2

A 15 kg bale of hay is tossed at 2.5 m/s² across a 2.0 m space onto a wagon. What's the amount of work done by the worker?

Solution

$$W = mad$$
$$= (15 \text{ kg}) (2.5 \text{ m/s}^2) (2.0 \text{ m})$$
$$= 75 \text{ J}$$

Example 3

A 75 kg object is pushed up a frictionless ramp at a constant velocity. The height of the ramp is 5.0 m, and its incline length is 10 m.

Solution

$$W = mad$$
$$= (75 \text{ kg}) (9.81 \text{ m/s}^2) (5.0 \text{ m})$$
$$= 3\ 678.75 \text{ J}$$
$$= 3.7 \times 10^3 \text{ J}$$

PRACTICE EXERCISE

1. Complete the following table by converting the given values.

J	kJ	MJ
		2.00×10^{-3}
	1.2×10^{-1}	
3.01		

2. Complete the following table by filling in the missing values.

m (kg)	a (m/s^2)	d (m)	W (J)
25	3.0		750
4.0	2.0	2.5	
	4.0	400	300

3. When a weightlifter holds a 125 kg mass 20 cm above his head for 3.0 s, what amount of work is done?

4. If you accelerate a 500 g mass at 12 m/s^2 for 10 m, how much work is done?

5. If a crane needs 1.7×10^3 J to lift a 1 000 kg crate 9.0 m high, what is the force exerted?

6. A 50 g lunch pail is lifted up 500 m. If the work required to do this was 1 450 J, what was the acceleration?

7. If 75 kg sprinter achieves a speed of 9.8 m/s from rest in a time of 1.3 s over a distance of 3.2 m, how much work was done?

8. If a 750 g mass is accelerated at a rate of 11.0 m/s^2 for a distance of 3.0 m, how much work was done?

9. An engine exerts 5.8×10^5 J to move a boat. The boat is moved with a force of 300 N. Find the mass of the boat if the acceleration is 6.01 m/s^2.

Lesson 7 POWER

NOTES

Measurements of power are important in everyday life. For example, electrical companies measure how much power homeowners use every month. At a person's place of work, he or she's normally judged by how much work is done in the time spent at work. These are measures of power.

Power is measured in Watts (J/s).

$$P = \frac{W}{t}$$

Power is the rate at which work is done. It can be measured in J/s, or watts.

$$P = \frac{W}{t}$$

where $P =$ power, measured in watts (J/s)
         $W =$ work, measured in joules (J)
         $t =$ time, measured in seconds (s)

Electrical power can also be measured using the formula below.

$$p = \frac{E}{t}$$

$$P = \frac{E}{t}$$

where $P =$ power, measured in watts (W)
         $E =$ electrical energy, measured in joules (J)
         $t =$ time, measured in seconds (s)

Electrical power is a measure of the amount of electrical energy passing through a wire in a given amount of time

Example 1

Find the amount of power needed to move a large desk up a ramp if it took 500 J of work to do it in 30.0 s.

Solution

$$P = \frac{W}{t}$$

$$= \frac{500 \text{ J}}{30.0 \text{ s}}$$

$$= 16.7 \text{ W}$$

Example 2

How much power is used if a 300 J appliance is on for 30.0 s?

Solution

$$P = \frac{E}{t}$$

$$= \frac{300 \text{ J}}{30.0 \text{ s}}$$

$$= 10.0 \text{ W}$$

PRACTICE EXERCISE

1. If a 100 W bulb is left on for 100 min, how much electrical energy is used?

2. **a)** If an appliance uses 5 000 J of energy over 10.0 min, what is the power demand of the appliance?

   b) If the appliance uses 12 000 J of energy, how long did it run?

3. A 55 kg man runs at a constant velocity up a ramp that is 2.5 m high in 3.0 s. What is his power output?

   A) 1.2×10^2 W   **B)** 4.5×10^2 W
   C) 5.3×10^2 W   **D)** 7.5×10^2 W

4. A 1.50×10^3 kg vehicle accelerates from rest to a velocity of 12.0 m/s in 4.0 s. What is the car's power output?

   A) 18 W   **B)** 72 W
   C) 2.7×10^3 W   **D)** 1.8×10^4 W

5. A 30 kg object is lifted 3.0 m straight up in 2.00 s by a woman. Find the power she used.

6. If it takes 40 watts to move a lawn mower for 30 minutes, what is the amount of work done?

7. It takes 50 W to move a universal gym bench press and the work done was 300 J. Find the amount of time it took to move the bench press.

Lesson 8   KINETIC ENERGY (E_k)

Forms of Energy

There are many different forms of energy. Remember that energy can be neither created nor destroyed, but it can be transferred between forms.

- Chemical – Energy stored in bonds, for example in batteries

- Electrical/Magnetic – Energy in current form as it passes through a wire or in the air; this is a flowing or kinetic energy

- Nuclear/Solar – Energy stored inside atoms; when the nucleus of an atom is changed by fission or fusion, large amounts of energy are released

- Mechanical/Heat – A combination of both stored (potential) and moving (kinetic) energy

- Heat (Thermal) – Energy that creates a flow from hot to cold areas; heat flow is studied by using the laws of thermodynamics

Types of Energy

Energy is either being stored or it is moving. Stored energy is called *potential energy*, and moving energy is called *kinetic energy*.

Kinetic energy is the energy that an object has as a result of its motion. The units of measurement of kinetic energy are Joules (J).

In mechanical systems, kinetic energy can be found by using the formula:

$$E_k = \frac{1}{2}mv^2, \quad \text{where} \quad m = \text{mass, in kg}$$
$$v = \text{velocity, in m/s}$$

Electrical energy flow can be measured using the formula:

$$E_k = Pt, \quad \text{where} \quad P = \text{power in watts (W)}$$
$$t = \text{time in seconds (s)}$$

Kinetic energy is the energy that an object has a result of its motion.

$$E_k = \frac{1}{2}mv^2$$

$$E_k = Pt$$

Example 1

Orin is running to the library at a speed of 4.0 m/s. His mass is 80.0 kg. Find his kinetic energy.

Solution

$$E_k = \frac{1}{2}mv^2$$

$$= \frac{1}{2}(80.0 \text{ kg})(4.0 \text{ m/s})^2$$

$$= 640 \text{ J}$$

Example 2

A washing machine uses 1 500 W to complete one cycle.
If the cycle takes 22.0 min, what was the kinetic energy used?

Solution

$$E_k = Pt$$

$$= (1\ 500 \text{ W})(22.0 \text{ min})(60 \text{ s/min})$$

$$= 1.98 \times 10^6 \text{ J}$$

PRACTICE EXERCISE

1. Mary runs home from her friend's house at a speed of 4.9 m/s. She weighs 48 kg. Determine the kinetic energy she expends.

2. If the speed of a 1.0 kg kitten is 5.0 m/s, what is its kinetic energy?

3. A 60.0 kg student is running at a constant speed of 3.50 m/s. Find the kinetic energy of the student.

4. If the kinetic energy of a 3.00 kg ball is 2.00×10^3 J, what is the speed of the ball

5. If a 50 kg girl jogs for 35 min at 3.5 m/s, what it her power output?

6. If it takes 400 W to run an electric drill for 1 min, what is the kinetic energy of the drill?

7. If 300 J of kinetic energy are required to run a vacuum cleaner for 250 s, how much power is needed?

8. If 325 000 J of energy were produced when a 300 W electric clothes dryer was used, what is the time in minutes that it took to dry the clothes?

9. If 5.5×10^6 J of kinetic energy were produced over 60 s by a 1.5×10^6 kg train, what is the distance the train travelled in 60 s?

Lesson 9 POTENTIAL ENERGY (E_p)

Potential energy is stored energy. Potential energy can be stored as
- gravitational energy
- elastic energy
- chemical energy
- electrical energy

This lesson will deal with gravitational, elastic, and electrical potential energy.

Potential energy is measured in joules (J) and can be calculated by multiplying the mass of an object by the gravitational constant and by the height at which the object rests.

Potential energy is $E_p = mgh$

Electrically, $E_p = qV$, which is charge (q), measured in coulombs, multiplied by voltage (V).

Example 1
A 20 kg ball is held at a height of 7.0 m.

a) Determine the ball's potential energy.

Solution

$$E_p = mgh$$
$$= (20 \text{ kg}) (9.81 \text{ m/s}^2) (7 \text{ m})$$
$$= 1\ 373.4 \text{ J}$$
$$= 1.4 \times 10^3 \text{ J}$$

b) The ball is dropped. What is the ball's potential energy when it hits the ground?

Solution

Since the ball cannot be dropped any farther, there is no potential energy.
$$E_p = mgh$$
$$= (20 \text{ kg})(9.81 \text{ m/s}^2)(0 \text{ m})$$
$$= 0$$

NOTES

$E_p = mgv$

$E_p = qV$

$E_p = mgh$

$E_p = qV$

Example 2

Determine the mass of an object that sits 100 m above the ground and has a potential energy of 5 000 J.

Solution

$$E_p = mgh$$
$$5\,000 \text{ J} = (m)\,(9.81 \text{ m/s}^2)\,(100 \text{ m})$$

$$m = \frac{5\,000 \text{ J}}{\left(9.81 \text{ m/s}^2\right)(100 \text{ m})}$$

$$= 5.1 \text{ kg}$$

Example 3

A 12.0 V battery has 500 J of electrical potential energy.
Determine the battery's charge.

Solution

$$E_p = qV$$
$$500 \text{ J} = q(12.0 \text{ V})$$

$$q = \frac{500 \text{ J}}{12.0 \text{ V}}$$

$$= 41.8 \text{ C}$$

PRACTICE EXERCISE

1. Energy stored is a)_____ energy and is measured in b)_____. The formula for this type of energy is c)_____. The formula for calculating electrical potential energy is d)_____ and this energy is measured in e)_____. Energy in motion is called f)_____ energy and is measured in g)_____. The formula for calculating this type of energy is h)_____.

2. A 400 kg mass of iron sitting on a barge is ready to fall 5.0 m into the ocean. Find the energy that would be released if it fell.

3. A large boulder weighing 500 kg is sitting on a ledge 10.0 m above the ground. What is its potential energy?

4. If a 120 V line is connected to a 20 C charge, how much energy will be used?

5. A battery has a charge of 100 C and a voltage of 9 V. What is its potential energy?

6. Complete the following chart by converting volts to charge to potential energy.

V	q	E_P
25	0.1	2.5
7.0	5.3×10^2	
19		1.9×10^2
	6.1	1.5×10^{-2}

7. Lane, a bow hunter, must pull his bow back with a force of 14 N over a distance of 20 cm to shoot an arrow. Determine the potential energy of the system.

8. The potential energy of an electrical system is 4.0×10^6 J and the voltage of the system is 220 V. Find the amount of the current.

9. A truck of unknown mass accidentally leaves the road and begins to fall over a 10 m cliff. If the potential energy of the truck is 2.5×10^5 J what is the mass of the truck?

10. It takes 3.94×10^7 J of energy to burn 1.00 kg of body fat. If Bob burns 2.00×10^6 J/h while jogging, how long will it take him to burn 3.50 kg of fat?

11. If a hydroelectric plant produces 5×10^9 J from a dam 60 m high, what is the mass of water passing through the turbines?

134

Lesson 10 MECHANICAL ENERGY ($E_k + E_p$)

Objects have both kinetic energy and potential energy. The amount of each type of energy depends on the amount of motion and the object's position.

$E_{\text{total mechanical energy}} = E_k + E_p$

In all transfers of energy from one form to another, energy is conserved. The total energy in a system is the sum of the kinetic energy and the potential energy. At any point in time, the energy is in either or both forms.

$$E_T = E_k + E_p$$

For example, Quentin accidentally kicks a ball over a cliff. As the ball falls, its energy shifts from almost all potential energy to almost all kinetic energy. On the way down, the proportion of kinetic energy grows as the ball's motion increases. The potential energy decreases as the ball's height decreases.

It is possible to find the initial kinetic energy, and potential energy and the final kinetic energy and potential energy in any system. The total initial energy equals the total final energy in any system.

In summary, E_p (initial) + E_k (initial) = E_p (final) + E_k (final).

At the beginning of a fall, kinetic energy = 0. At the end of the fall, potential energy = 0. Therefore,

$$mgh_i + \frac{1}{2}mv^2_i = mgh_f + \frac{1}{2}mv^2_f$$

$$mgh_i + 0 = 0 + \frac{1}{2}mv^2_f$$

$$mgh_i = \frac{1}{2}mv^2_f$$

$$E_p = mgh \text{ (initial)} = E_k = \frac{1}{2}mv^2 \text{ (final)}$$

Since mass is found on both sides of this equation, it can be cancelled out. Therefore,

$$gh_i = \frac{1}{2}v^2_f$$

(gravitational constant) (height) = $\frac{1}{2}$ (final velocity)^2

Example 1

A bow string is pulled back 0.45 m with a force of 75 N. What is the potential energy of a 0.050 kg arrow at the highest position if the arrow is fired vertically into the air.

Solution
To find the potential energy, first to determine the work done on the bow.

$$W = Fd$$
$$= (75 \text{ N})(0.45 \text{ m})$$
$$= 33.8 \text{ J}$$

The potential energy stored in the bow is equal to the amount of work done on the bow since this potential energy is elastic.

When the arrow is released, the change in kinetic energy (E_k) is equal to the elastic stored energy (E_p). The kinetic energy is also equal to 33.8 J.

As the arrow slows when it reaches its highest point, the energy is reconverted to gravitational potential energy, $E_p = 33.8$ J.

The highest point that the arrow reaches can be determined using $E_p = 33.8$ J if the mass of the arrow is known.

$$E_p = mgh$$
$$33.8 \text{ J} = m(9.81 \text{ m/s}^2)(h)$$

If the arrow has a mass of 0.050 kg, then the arrow will reach a height of

$$h = \frac{33.8 \text{ J}}{(0.050 \text{ kg})(9.81 \text{ m/s})^2}$$
$$= 69 \text{ m}$$

Pendulums (Harmonic Systems)

Pendulums exemplify the transfer of potential and kinetic energy. Work is done to lift the swinging ball. The ball gains gravitational potential energy. When released, the potential energy is transferred into kinetic energy. When the ball is at its lowest point, all of the energy is kinetic and is equal to the original potential energy.

As the pendulum rises, it slows and the kinetic energy is transferred back into potential energy. When the pendulum is swinging in a vacuum, it will continue swinging back and forth for a long time.
The energy transfer is almost perfect.

E_{Pmax}

E_{kmax}

Example 2

If an object falls at a velocity of 10 m/s, what is the height from which it fell?

Solution

Hint: Remember that mass cancels in both E_k and E_p.

$$gh = \frac{1}{2}v^2$$

$$h = \frac{\frac{1}{2}v^2}{g}$$

$$= \frac{\frac{1}{2}(10 \text{ m/s})^2}{9.81 \text{ m/s}^2}$$

$$= 5.1 \text{ m}$$

Example 3

If an object falls from a height 10 m, what is its velocity?

Solution

$$gh = \frac{1}{2}v^2$$

$$v = \sqrt{2(gh)}$$

$$= \sqrt{2(9.81 \text{ m/s}^2)(10 \text{ m})}$$

$$= 14 \text{ m/s downward}$$

Example 4

In a pendulum system, the mass of the ball is 0.200 kg and the vertical height difference between the top and the bottom of the swing is 2.0 m. Determine the potential energy (at the top) and velocity (at the bottom) of the swing.

Solution

$$E_p = mgh$$
$$= (0.200 \text{ kg}) (2.0 \text{ m}) (9.81 \text{ m/s}^2)$$
$$= 3.9 \text{ J}$$

$$E_k = E_p = 3.9 \text{ J}$$

$$E_k = \frac{1}{2}mv^2$$

$$v = \sqrt{\frac{2(3.9 \text{ J})}{0.200 \text{ kg}}}$$

$$= 6.3 \text{ m/s}$$

Example 5

If a 20 g rock is thrown up at a velocity of 30 m/s, how high will it go?

Solution

$$E_k = E_p$$

$$gh = \frac{1}{2}v^2$$

$$h = \frac{\frac{1}{2}(30 \text{ m/s})^2}{9.81 \text{ m/s}^2}$$

$$= 46 \text{ m}$$

PRACTICE EXERCISE

1. A 50 kg dog is sitting on a step that is 15 cm high.

   a) Calculate the potential energy of the dog.

   b) The dog steps onto the floor. Determine the velocity of the dog as he touches the floor.

2. If Jay drops a 5.0 kg rock from the top of the school gym (12 m high), what will the velocity of the rock be just before impact?

3. If a system has 50 J of energy in both kinetic energy and potential energy and it fluctuates between these forms, what kind of system is it?

4. Determine how high a 190 g baseball will go if thrown straight up at 20 m/s.

5. A ball falls from the top of a ladder, hits the ground, and bounces up it loses 10% of its energy on every bounce. The initial height of the ball was 3.5 m, and the ball weighs 1.0 kg.
   Determine the energy at the top of the third bounce.

6. A person uses a sling shot to fire an 0.50 N rock straight up into the to a height of 35 m.
   Find the speed of the rock as it first left the sling shot.

7. A 30 kg girl bounces on a trampoline and gains 500 J of gravitational potential energy at the top of the bounce.

a) Find the amount of elastic potential energy in the trampoline when she first jumped.

b) How high did she jump?

Lesson 11 THERMODYNAMICS

Natural Energy Conversions

Sunlight is solar energy that is from nuclear fusion reactions in the sun.
When photons reach the atmosphere, about 30% are reflected into space.
The remaining 70% are absorbed by Earth and its atmosphere.
Only 1% of this energy reaches the plants of Earth, where it is transferred
into chemical potential energy by photosynthesis. When animals consume
this potential energy, it is converted into ATP, a nucleotide that stores and
transports chemical energy. ATP is then used to produce movements in
the animal.
This kinetic energy has a byproduct of heat or thermal energy, which is
released into the atmosphere.

Man-made energy transfer, such as power plants, and generate massive
amounts of electricity from falling water, burning coal, or nuclear
reactions. Each of these is designed to change some form of energy into
electrical energy for our everyday use.

Thermodynamics

Thermodynamics is the study of the relationships of heat, work and energy.
Two of the four laws of thermodynamics are given below, which were
developed over many years.

First Law of Thermodynamics

The First Law of Thermodynamics states that energy is neither created nor
destroyed, only converted to another form in a system. Nuclear potential
energy is changed in a reactor to thermal energy. This heat is then used to
boil water, which in turn drives a steam generator to produce electricity.

Second Law of Thermodynamics

According to the Second Law of Thermodynamics, heat will always flow
from a higher to a lower temperature. Warm air will flow toward cooler
air as it does in weather systems. Hot steam will rise to cooler altitudes.
Hot water will flow toward cooler water as it does in ocean currents.

Energy Efficiency

The amount of heat lost during energy transformation is an indicator of the
efficiency of the system. The less heat lost, the more efficient the system.

Energy efficiency is measured by using the formula below.

$$\text{Efficiency } \% \frac{\text{Output Energy}}{\text{Input Energy}} \times 100$$

If the output energy of a system is 300 J and the input energy is 200 J, then the efficiency is

$$\frac{300 \text{ J}}{200 \text{ J}} \times 100 = 150\%$$

For example when the sun's energy is used by plants that produce a crop, the efficiency of the photosynthesis in that crop can be determined by measuring and comparing the sun's energy with the energy of the crop.

Given the sun's input energy as 5.0×10^5 J and the crop yield as 8.0×10^5 J, what was the energy efficiency of this system?

$$\text{Efficiency} = \frac{8.0 \times 10^5 \text{ J}}{5.0 \times 10^5 \text{ J}} \times 100 = 160\%$$

The only system that can generate light and heat at an efficiency greater than 100% is a nuclear fusion reaction found in stars, including our sun. It is so hot at the centre of a star that larger atoms are created from smaller ones. All other energy systems are less than 100% efficient.

Useful mechanical efficiency is a measure of the amount of energy that a machine actually uses to move an object compared with the amount of energy that the machine uses. Useful mechanical efficiency is found by dividing the useful energy or work by the total mechanical energy or work, multiplied by 100 to give a % value.

Some examples of use full mechanical efficiency calculations are given below.

- An SUV using gasoline as fuel inputs 675 kJ and outputs 81 kJ. The efficiency is:
$$\frac{81 \text{ kJ}}{675 \text{ kJ}} \times 100 = 12\%$$

- A fluorescent light uses 125 kJ of electrical energy to produce 27.5 kJ of light energy. The efficiency is:
$$\frac{27.5 \text{ kJ}}{125 \text{ kJ}} \times 100 = 22\%$$

- A regular light bulb uses 780 J of electrical energy to produce 31 J of light energy. The efficiency is:
$$\frac{31 \text{ J}}{780 \text{ J}} \times 100 = 4.0\%$$

- A natural gas furnace uses 110 MJ to produce 85 MJ of heat.
  The efficiency is:

$$\frac{85 \text{ MJ}}{110 \text{ MJ}} \times 100 = 77\%$$

Limits to Efficiency

All energy-related systems that exist on Earth are limited to some degree because the earth is an open system. Friction and entropy cause reactions to release energy. Much of the lost energy is lost into the atmosphere.

Motor engines create heat which is released from the system.
They create exhaust gases which are hot and contain unburned fuel molecules.
Engine lubricants help to decrease friction between moving parts in a machine or engine, but they too break down with time. This decreases the efficiency and increases energy use. It takes more energy to do something if the friction increases. This is why it is important to keep your car in tune and well lubricated.

Insulation can help to increase efficiency, especially when heating your home in a cold climate. Insulation also helps in electrical transmission lines. When the lines are insulated, less energy is lost to the environment.

All insulating materials are given an R-value. This R-value is a number that represents the heat retention ability of the material. If the R-number is high, then it is a good insulator.

Packed snow has an R-value of 60 so it can save a life in a storm.
Making a snow house and getting inside will allow the inside temperature to rise by at least 30°C.

Regular home pink fiberglass insulation only has an R-value of 30.

PRACTICE EXERCISE

1. Energy is measured in

   A) Joules
   C) Velocity

   B) Newtons
   D) Watts

2. Which of the following amounts is equivalent to 1 J?

   A) 1 W × s
   C) 1 V × s

   B) 1 W/s
   D) 1 V/s

3. Energy efficiency is measured in

   A) Coulombs
   C) Volts

   B) Watts
   D) Percentage

4. The energy efficiency of a small truck is about

   A) 4%
   C) 22%

   B) 12%
   D) 77%

5. Write the energy efficiency formula.

6. For each of the following inputs and outputs, determine the efficiency.

   a) Input = 120 J, Output = 12 J

   b) Input = 5 J, Output = 0.1 J

c) Input = 150 000 J, Output = 20 000 J

d) Input = 54 J, Output = 15 J

e) Input = 12 000 J, Output = 100 J

7. Which of the efficiencies determined in question 6 is highest (most efficient)?

8. Determine the missing value.

a) Output E = 100 J, Efficiency = 0%

Input E =

b) Input E = 100 J, Efficiency = 30%

Output E =

c) Output E = 120 000 J, Efficiency = 2%

Input E =

9. State the two laws of thermodynamics and explain the effect of each of them relative to a boiling pot of water.

10. Why is a perpetual motion machine impossible to build?

11. a) Determine the efficiency of a machine that has an output of 5.5 J and that uses 1.5 J of energy to achieve that output.

   b) Is it possible to have such a machine?

12. Determine the efficiency of a system whose output is 5.0 W and input is 23.5 W.

Lesson 12   HEAT ENGINES

Over many years inventors and scientists have build upon one another's ideas, regarding the laws of thermodynamics. As these laws have been more clearly understood, new and realistic adaptations, such as the development of the heat engine, for their application have been developed.

As engines were designed they begin to replace human and animal labour. The main advantage of engine over human and animal labour is that it can work continuously until needing repair or replacement.

- Christian Huygens experimented with gunpowder engines in 1680.

- The steam pump was invented by Thomas Savery in 1698, and, since that time, steam power has been used in all major industries.

- The first internal combustion engine is believed to have been invented in 1801 by Philippe Lebon. His engine used coal as a heat source.
  Later gasoline replaced coal, but the principle remained the same.

With the invention of a portable power supply, people adapted the engine to many different devices.

For example, aircrafts came into being in the 1890s when engines that could generate enough kinetic energy to overcome the weight of the craft were developed. Most of the weight of an aircraft is in the engine and fuel reserve. Turbojets, designed and used after the second World War, have been replaced with turbofan engines, which are far more efficient.
The ability to cross oceans and continents is becoming still more efficient as newer jet engines are adapted to better-designed aircraft that can carry more people and cargo.

- Injection
- Ignition
- Expansion
- Stage 4 is exhaust release

Combustion Engines

All internal combustion engines have internal moving parts. An internal combustion engine has at least one hollow cylinder in which fuel is ignited. The burning fuel increases the air pressure inside the cylinder and forces a piston to move. The piston is attached to a crank shaft that turns as the piston moves. Once the piston hits the bottom of the cylinder, it begins to move back up to start another cycle of the engine. As the piston nears the top of the cylinder, fuel is injected into the space and ignited.
As the piston goes down the cylinder, exhaust gas is released through a hole in the cylinder. This cycle is repeated many times per minute. Lawnmowers use single cylinder engines.

Each cycle of an engine involves two or four steps. Below is an illustration of a four step engine.

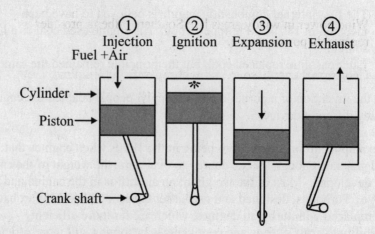

In a four-stroke engine, the stages are:

-     stage 1 – the fuel and air injection
-     stage 2 – ignition
-     stage 3 – expansion
-     stage 4 – exhaust release

When a number of cylinders are lined up together and are attached to the same crankshaft, the movement of the shaft is continuous.
Power generated by each cylinder will keep the shaft turning even when it is attached to a load, such as a car going up a hill.

Increasing the size of the cylinder and piston will increase the power of the engine. More gas applied to the cylinder will cause a bigger explosion and turn the crankshaft more quickly. For example, in a car, when the gas pedal is pushed, more gas enters the cylinder and the car accelerates.

Energy Demand and Use

For the past several hundred years, world energy demand has increased continuously. As the population of the world is continues to increase, so too will the demand for energy. Alternate energy sources need to be developed to take the place of oil, coal, and natural gas as supplies decrease. Current coal reserves are only expected to last for another 200 years, natural gas reserves for 62 years, and oil reserves for 40 years.

A number of alternative energy sources are being considered more fully.

- Fuel cells that convert hydrogen to electrical energy are now being introduced into vehicles.

- Solar power is becoming more useful and is a limitless source of power.

- Wind power in windy areas like Southern Alberta provides a renewable power source.

- Geothermal energy sources are cheap, safe, and endless.

PRACTICE EXERCISE

Use the following diagram of an engine to answer the following questions.

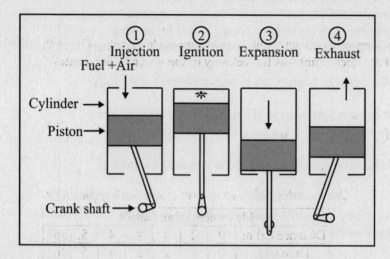

1. What is the purpose of the valves?

2. Why must the walls of the engine be thick?

3. As an engine gets hot, the cylinders, being made of metal, expand.
   How can the cylinders be prevented from expanding too much?

4. If exhaust is not cleared from the engine, what will result?

5. Fighter aircraft of the Second World War had a problem with their engines. They flew at high altitudes and had to fly at high speeds with tight turns. What might have caused this problem?

6. Design an engine using injection, ignition, expansion, and exhaust stages.

7. If engine heat gets too high, what can happen to the engine?

150

PRACTICE TEST

1. From where is the major form of energy used in creating plant sugars initially derived?

2. The stars below represent contact points of a water spider's tracks. Given that the interval contact points are equal at which point was the velocity of the water spider greatest?

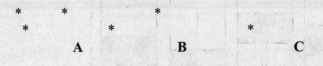

Use the table below to answer the following questions.

Movement of an Object							
Distance (*d*) m	0	2	4	4	4	5	6
Time (*t*) s	0	1	2	3	4	5	6

3. **a)** Plot the distance vs. time graph for the object's data

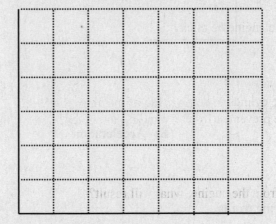

b) At which interval was the object moving fastest?

c) What was occurring between 3 and 4 seconds?

4. Describe the velocity variable in the following graphs.

a)

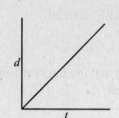

b)

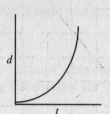

c)

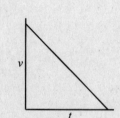

d)

e)

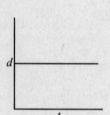

f)

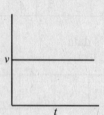

5. Slope can be calculated from

A) Velocity   **B)** Acceleration
C) Rise/run

6. Define each of the following words.

a) Energy –

b) Work –

c) Power –

d) Acceleration –

Use the following graph to answers questions 7 to 10.

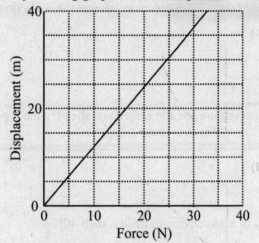

7. What does the area under the line represent?

8. What is the force at 10 m?

9. What is the slope of the line?

10. What is the displacement at 30 N?

11. Is work done when no movement occurs? Explain.

12. If a force of 5.5 N is applied over a 10 m distance, what is the work done?

13. When gasoline burns in a car engine and the car moves ahead, what type of energy is produced?

14. What causes the efficiency of a gas engine to be less than 40%?

15. The energy used by a particular triathlete in running is 2.5×10^6 J/h; in biking, it is 3.6×10^6 J/h; in swimming, it is 5.5×10^6 J/h. If the triathlete runs for 1.0 h, bikes for 45 min, and swims for 30 min, what is the total energy used?

16. If the triathlete in question 15 burns 4.0×10^7 J of energy for every kg of fat, how much fat does she burn during the triathlon?

17. If a force of 45 N applied over 1.5 km, how much work is done?

18. What is the kinetic energy of a 0.200 kg ball travelling at 4.0 m/s?

19. If the kinetic energy of a runner is 45 J and he is moving at 1.5 m/s, what is the mass of the runner?

20. What do the symbols *mgh* represent?

21. When energy is stored in a battery, what form is it in?

22. What is the formula for electrical potential energy?

23. If the amount of energy stored in a 12 V battery is 500 J, what is the charge (*q*)?

24. The units of measure of a Watt are

    A) $kg \times m^2/s^2$ **B)** m/s^2
    C) $N \times m$ **D)** J/s

25. A pendulum that has a 0.02 kg bob reaches a velocity of 3.0 m/s at the bottom of the swing. What is the highest position it reaches?

NOTES

CYCLING OF MATTER IN LIVING SYSTEMS

When you are finished this unit, you will be able to demonstrate an understanding of...

- a cell as the basic unit of living systems
- structures and functions of the cell and cells types, including prokaryotes and eukaryotes by the use of magnification
- growth features of living systems, the limitations of systems based on surface area and volume ratios
- cell division, muliticellularity, division of roles in plant and animal cells using technology
- a cell as an open system that exchanges energy and matter with the environment, using concentration gradients, semipermeability, photosynthesis, the CO_2 cycle, ATP use and production
- laboratory investigations of the cell
- energy and matter needs of a cell that are dealt with at a distance from the cell's surface
- structural diversity allowing multicellular organisms to live
- energy exchanges in multicellular organisms via transport, nutrient acquisition, excretion, gas exchange, cytoplasmic streaming, and water movements using technology

Lesson 1 HISTORY

The idea of spontaneous generation was popular among scientists in the Middle Ages. This theory stated that all life started from non-life. The absence of microscopes coupled with a belief in mysticism allowed this theory to remain popular until the 1860s.

In 1668, Francesco Redi questioned this theory as a result of a simple experiment he compared covered and uncovered meat. The meat that was covered with the cloth remained free of fly larva (maggots), whereas, the uncovered meat developed maggots quickly.

In 1745, Lazzaro Spallanzani stated that micro-organisms in the air were responsible for maggot growth on the meat. He repeated the meat experiment but put the meat in a vacuum. No growth occurred.

In 1859, the French Academy of Science started a contest to finally prove or disprove the theory of spontaneous generation. Louis Pasteur eventually won the contest in 1864.

Life starts from similar life.

Pasteur developed an "S"-shaped glass tube that allowed air into a beaker filled with beef broth. Although air could enter the beaker, wind, bugs, and airborne particles could not. No spontaneous growth occurred in the beaker. To discount anyone saying he had killed the micro-organisms in the broth. Pasteur did a control experiment by setting up a beaker without an "S" tube; growth did occur in this beaker. Pasteur even went as far as to test an empty "S" beaker. No spontaneous growth occurred there either. It was finally accepted that life starts from other similar life.

Controlled variables:
The variables that are kept the same

To clearly see how science works, we need to prove that the results of an experiment can be trusted.

Manipulated variable:
A variable that is changed (manipulated)

Responding variable:
reacts to the changes in the manipulated variable

In analyzing the experiment, we see that Pasteur kept the broth, the light and temperature. These are called *controlled variables*. He manipulated, or changed, only one thing in this experiment: the access of air to the flask. This is called the *manipulated variable*. He then did the experiment looking for any response. The *responding variable*, of course, was the growth of mould on the broth. On the open broth, mould grew; on the empty, clean flask, no mould grew; and on the flask with the "S" tube, no mould grew.

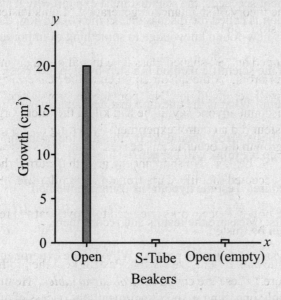

S-tube

Air

PASTEUR'S BEAKER

Broth

Pasteur's results can be graphed as shown below.

Growth of Mould on Beef Broth by Container Type.

In scientific theory, the manipulated variable is graphed on the *abscissa* or *x*-axis. The responding variable is graphed along the *ordinate* or *y*-axis of a graph.

NOTES

Scientific Method:
- Problem
- Hypothesis
- Procedure
- Results
- Analysis
- Conclusion

Scientific Method

Today, scientists must go through a strict process when they do experiments to test a theory. This process is called the Scientific Method. When a new theory is put forth, every aspect of it must be tested.

Each test must start off with a problem. A problem is any question that needs a proven answer. The next step is the hypothesis. A hypothesis is what the scientists think should happen if she does the experiment, and provides an explanation for the answer. The actual test is called the procedure and must be controlled so that there are no mistakes.

In an experiment, all conditions — except one — are strictly controlled so that they are the same for every trial of the experiment. These variables called the *controlled variables*. The exception is the one condition that is changed for each trial; it is called the *manipulated variable*.

In any experiment, there can only be one manipulated variable.

In the experiment, the scientist looks for an answer but must always be objective. If the experiment fails, the scientist must explain why it failed. If the experiment succeeds, the scientist must explain why it succeeded. This explanation is called the discussion. In the conclusion, the scientist may apply this new-found knowledge to something of importance.

The format of the scientific method is a step-by-step process.

1. Problem: What is the question that needs an answer?

2. Hypothesis: How should we try to solve the problem? What do we think will happen?

3. Procedure: Test the hypothesis using the method.

4. Results: Measure the results and record them.

5. Analysis: Discuss the results. Why did the experiment succeed or fail?

6. Conclusion: What are the applications of the new knowledge, or what is a possible new test method if it did not work.

PRACTICE EXERCISE

1. Who won the contest sponsored by the French Academy of Science and proved the theory of spontaneous generation wrong?

   A) Spallanzani   **B)** Redi

   C) Needham   **D)** Pasteur

2. In a graph, on which axis is the controlled variable plotted?

3. What are responding variables? Give an example.

4. List the steps of the scientific method in proper order.

5. Plot the data below. It is from an experiment that compared cell growth of colony *A* and colony *B*. Provide the appropriate labels and title.

Number of cells	Time in hours					
	1	2	3	4	5	6
Colony *A*	1	2	3	4	5	6
Colony *B*	1	3	5	7	9	11

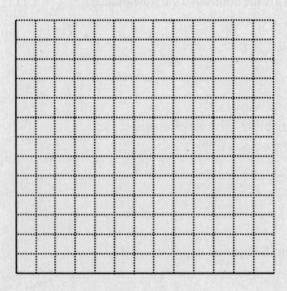

6. Insect larvae grow on exposed animal tissue. During this growth, they go through normal stages of development, namely: egg, larva, pupa, and adult. Each stage of development takes a specific amount of time, so they can be used as a "biological clock" to determine exactly when the tissue was left exposed.

	Egg	Larva	Pupa	Adult
Time	1.0 h	12.0 h	26.0 h	48.0 h

Determine the manipulated variable and responding variable for this experiment, and then graph below. Provide the appropriate labels and title.

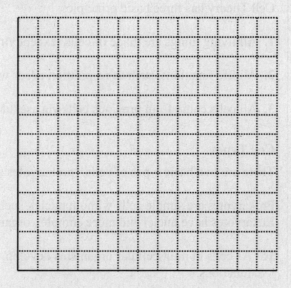

Lesson 2 CELL THEORY AND CELL TYPES

Cell Theory

Cells were not known by scientists until the idea of a cell was first posed by Robert Brown in the 1830s as he studied orchids. In 1838, Matthias Jakob Schleiden proposed that all plants are made up of cells. Later, Theodor Schwann did the same for animals. Lastly, Rudolf Virchow stated that cells come only from pre–existing cells.

Cell Theory has three basic principles:

1. All living things are made of cells (except viruses)

2. All life functions, such as respiration occur within cells

3. All cells come from previous cells via asexual or sexual reproduction

Cell Types

There are two basic types of cells: prokaryotes and eukaryotes.

Prokaryotes are simple cells without nuclei, such as bacteria. Eukaryotes have nuclei and more complex organelles, such as skin cells.

1. As cells in multicellular organisms develop, they take on specific functions.

2. Each of these functions helps the organism stay alive, reproduce, and develop.

3. Each organism that has developed takes on a specific role in the environment in which it lives. All organisms interact in their own biome.

4. Because we were not around when these organisms came into being, we try to determine how each organism fits into the puzzle of life.

In order to determine how all the parts of our world fit together, scientists developed a classification system for all life forms.

All living things are classified by their characteristics into Kingdoms, Phyla, Classes, Orders, Families, Genera, and Species. This allows comparisons to be made between life forms. The cells that make up these organisms can be compared for common traits and functions. This kind of work has led to the discovery of new molecules that can help in medicine and agriculture. Furthermore, classifying organisms helps scientists learn what each individual cell and species contributes to our world so they can predict and prepare for changes that occur in nature.

Classification of life forms:
• Kingdom
• Phylum
• Class
• Order
• Family
• Genus
• Species

PRACTICE EXERCISE

1. Who was the person who thought that all cells come from other cells?

   A) Brown   **B)** Schleiden

   C) Schwann   **D)** Virchow

2. List the classifications of life forms in the correct order from Kingdom down.

3. The primary difference between a prokaryote and an eukaryote is that

   A) prokaryotes have a cell membrane, but eukaryutes do not

   B) eukaryotes have a cell membrane, but prokaryotes do not

   C) prokaryotes have a nucleus, but eukaryotes do not

   D) eukaryotes have a nucleus , but prokaryotes do not

4. What type of cells would all animal cells be classified as? Why are red blood cells not considered to be of the other type since they do not contain DNA?

5. Given all of the cows in the world, devise a classification for them.

6. Using your research skills and the organism classification system, find the genus and species names for a mountain lion (cougar).

Lesson 3   CELLS — STAINING AND IMAGING

To study cells, new methods had to be developed. Microscopes were built to see these building blocks of life. Unfortunately, cells are easy to see under microscopes unless they are properly treated or lit up.

Staining

Staining is a process whereby various chemicals are put on cells. Each staining chemical reacts with and colours one part of the cell. Some stains work well on the cell membranes and walls. Others work well on the nucleus or the other organelles of the cell. An example of a stain is iodine, which is used to detect the presence of starch in a cell. Under a microscope, plant cells stained with iodine have reddish-brown spots wherever starch is located.

Stains kill or fix cells.

The problem with these stains is that they normally kill the cell when they are applied. They "fix" the cell at the point of death. If an experiment is done to see how a cell reacts to the addition of a chemical, many cells must be used and sacrificed at different time intervals. This allows a process to be observed, such as a series of stop-action photographs.

A theory comes from repeated observations.

Laws are developed from tested theories that are true.

If we used iodine to measure starch production in a plant, we would first expose the leaves to light. Then, every 10 minutes, we would take part of a leaf and stain it for starch and put it under a microscope. We would then record the amount of starch we could see. Once we trust the method, we could manipulate the amount or type of light, the amount or type of nutrients the plant gets, or other items that we wanted to test. If we did this many times, we develop a theory. If many investigators did this and proved the theory to be true each time, we would have developed a law of science.

Illumination

There are several ways to project light onto cells. However, if the light is too direct, the image of the cell is too bright. If the light is projected from the sides, a contrast or shadow is created and the organelles can be seen more clearly. If the cells are stained with a fluorescent dye, then bright images of the cells and their parts can be seen under a fluorescent microscope. If the correct stain is used, system can actually be traced.

NOTES

Resolution

Once the cell has been magnified, the ability to distinguish between structures of the cell is necessary. Human eyes have a resolution of 0.1 nm, but are not strong enough to see the inside of plant and animal cells (except for large eggs).

On a computer screen, the number of pixels per centimeter is a measure of determining resolution. We cannot increase the number of pixels or rods and cones in our eyes. But, with the aid of lenses, the magnification can be increased. Hans Zachary Jansen did exactly that by inventing a compound microscope in the 1600s.

nm = nanometre
$1 \text{ nm} = 1 \times 10^{-9} \text{ m}$

Magnification

Magnification is the increase in the size of the image produced in a microscope. It can be determined using the formula:

$$\frac{\text{Low power magnification}}{\text{High power magnification}} = \frac{\text{High power field of view size}}{\text{Low power field of view size}}$$

Example 1

If, for a particular microscope, the low power magnification is 1, the high power magnification is 40.0 and the low power field of view is 2.0 cm, what is high power field of view?

Solution

$$\frac{1}{40.0} = \frac{x}{2.0 \text{ cm}}$$

$$x = \frac{2.0 \text{ cm}}{40.0} = 0.05 \text{ cm}$$

Magnification can also be determined using a simple lens power formula, where the total magnification is equal to the product of the lens magnification.

Magnification = Optical lens power × Objective lens power

For example, a 20 power lens used with an ocular lens (the eye piece) of 10 power gives a magnification of
$10 \times 20 = 200$ power.

Magnification = Optical lens power × Objective lens power

NOTES

Microscopes

Only a cell that has been properly stained and illuminated, a microscope is used to magnify the image of the cell. The parts of a microscope are listed below.

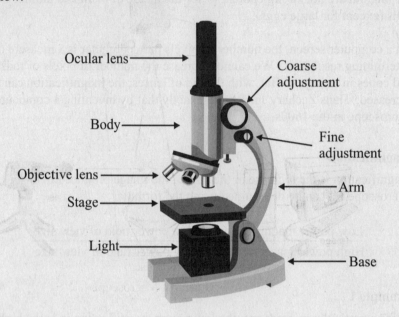

μm = micrometre

μm = 1×10^{-6} m

Light Microscopes

Light microscopes use light to illuminate cells on the stage of the microscope. These microscopes have a resolution of about 0.2 μm (0.000 000 2 m). This is about one half of the wavelength of visible light. Light microscopes come in six different types, each one adapted to resolve specific stains.

- Simple source microscopes — single lens to magnify; useful for large objects
- Dark field microscopes — blocks direct light and illuminates from the side; allows a bright cell to be viewed on a black background
- Phase contrast microscopes — separates direct and diffracted (scattered) light from specimen; specimen can be alive
- Polarized microscopes — light is filtered to allow only parallel light rays through the specimen, clearer image
- Compound microscopes — two lenses, maximum magnification is 1 000 times
- Fluorescent microscopes (UV light) — uses ultraviolet light on specimen, allowing organelles to glow in UV spectrum; especially useful when using fluorescent dyes

In the late 1980s laser technology, computers, and compound light microscopes were combined to produce confocal microscopes. These allow for live, wet-mounted specimens to be observed.

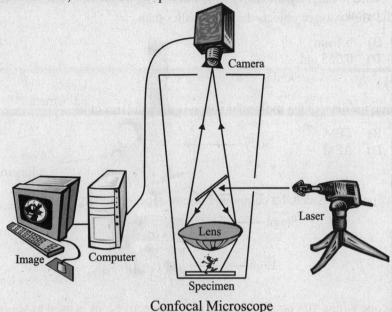

Confocal Microscope

Electron Microscopes

With the ability to bring into focus atomic particles using electricity (such as in televisions), scientists learned to combine particle emitters as a light source and electromagnets as lenses. The image is projected onto a fluorescent screen and then digitalized. This technique allows the magnification to increase to 500 000 times and the resolution to go to 0.1 nm, or 2 000 times better than light microscopes.

There are several types of electron microscopes:

SEM — Scanning Electron Microscope, which can only image surfaces.
TEM — Transmission Electron Microscope, which look at slices of specimens
STM — Scanning Tunneling Microscope, which can detect molecular shapes
AFM — Atomic Force Microscope

The AFM and STM give better resolution than the SEM and TEM.

In a crime lab, electron microscopes are used to examine particles found at crime scenes. They compare these particles with evidence taken from suspects. Once it is proven by electron microscopic evidence that the suspect and crime are related, it is very hard to disprove this.

PRACTICE EXERCISE

1. Light microscopes have the ability to see objects that are smaller than

   A) $0.2 \, \mu m$ **B)** $0.1 \, \mu m$

   C) $0.05 \, \mu m$ **D)** $0.025 \, \mu m$

2. The best type of microscope for detecting a molecular shape is with the use of a

   A) SEM   **B)** TEM

   C) STM   **D)** AFM

3. Would a confocal microscope be considered a compound microscope? Explain.

4. A compound light microscope with a 10× ocular lens and a 20× objective lens is used to see blood cells with a field of view of 0.5 mm. The largest white blood cell occupies one-quarter of the field of view.

   a) Calculate the diameter of the cell.

   b) If the image of the cell is 1.5 cm, what is it the magnification?

5. A small dust particle is examined under a microscope with a field of view of 0.5 mm and lenses of 5× and 20×. The image is $\frac{1}{3}$ of the view.

   a) Determine the diameter of the particle in μm.

   b) If the diameter of the particle is 0.5 mm, what is the magnification used?

6. In a light microscope, why is it important to have good lenses?

7. Describe how each of these microscopes work.

   a) Simple

   b) Compound

   c) Dark field

   d) Phase contrast

   e) Polarized

   f) Fluorescent

Lesson 4   GENE MAPPING

The nuclei of cells are known to contain the genetic material of cells. This is the hereditary information for each cell of an organism.

Genetic material is made up of DNA (deoxyribonucleic acid). DNA is a string of thousands of protein molecules lined up end to end twisted together into a double-helix shape. The two strands of proteins are held together by base pairs.

Bases:
A — Adenine
T — Thymine
C — Cytosine
G — Guanine

- thymine (T)
- guanine (G)
- cytosine (C)
- adenine (A)

Each strand contributes a sequence of bases. Each of these bases can only be joined to a complementary base from the other strand.
Complementary base pairs are:

Adenine — Thymine
A — T
and
Guanine — Cytosine
G — C

Complementary base pairs:

A — T
C — G

Therefore, a seemingly random series of base pairs runs down the centre of a double–helix.

DOUBLE HELIX

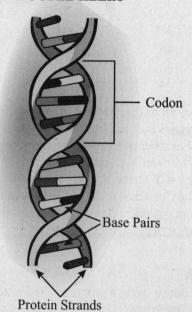

Codon

Base Pairs

Protein Strands

These base pairs are lined up along each DNA strand in what looks like random order. However, groups of these base pairs are used as a code for sending messages to the cell and to other cells. They are called codons. Each codon has three base pairs in it. A group of codons together will send a specific message to the cell. If a cell gets damaged and needs a new cell membrane, the DNA will instruct new molecules to form. These codons together act as a gene.

Codon — three base pairs
Gene — group of codons
along a strand

The sequence of genes in DNA is very specific to each species. Each species is said to have its own genotype. Genotype is the genetic code that is passed from parent to offspring of each species.

The strands of DNA are bunched up together to form *chromosomes*. A chromosome is a linear thread that carries many genes.

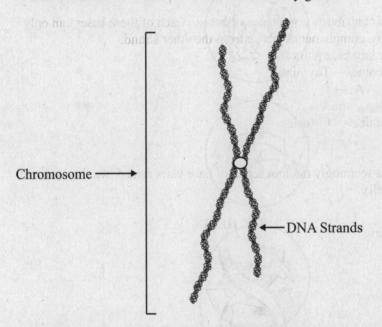

Coiled DNA —
chromosome

Chromosome ⟶

⟵ DNA Strands

During reproduction, all of the chromosomes in the nucleus are reproduced. The strands coil and become visible. During reproduction in humans, the normal number of visible chromosome pairs is 23. Most of these pairs form an X-shape, as depicted above. In males, the 23rd pair of chromosomes is Y-shaped. Each chromosome is responsible for carrying the hereditary material to its offspring and for producing all of the characteristics that an organism has, such as hair colour, skin tone, etc. These obvious characteristics are called phenotypes.

Cell Reproduction

Cells normally reproduce using a process called mitosis. Mitosis is a form of binary fission. Binary fission is asexual cellular reproduction. One parent cell produces two individual daughter cells.

NOTES

Stages of Mitosis:
- Interphase
- Prophase
- Metaphase
- Anaphase
- Telophase

Stages of Mitosis

1. Interphase

2. Prophase

3. Metaphase

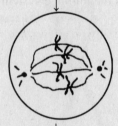

4. Anaphase

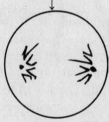

Daughter Cells

5. Telophase

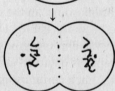 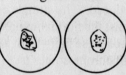

In cell mitosis, the exact copy of the parent cell is created.
These cells grow until they are the same size as the parent cell.
Daughter cells go through mitosis when they reproduce.
This process occurs over and over as a fetus grows into an adult.

During interphase, the cell prepares itself for division. The DNA replicates and coils into visible chromosomes. These chromosomes then pair up during prophase. There are 23 pairs of chromosomes in human cells.

During anaphase, the chromosome pairs migrate to each end of the cell. Once the chromosomes reach the poles, a new cell membrane forms and cuts the parent cell into two daughter cells in telophase.
These chromosomes of the daughter cells are exact duplicates of those in the parent cell.

The Human Genome Project

In the early 1990s it was decided that the exact sequencing for human DNA codes (genes) was to be found. This project was called the Human Genome Project and is now complete. The information gathered now helps scientists and doctors to solve genetic problems. It also helps in research on aging and normal cell functions. If scientists can determine normal life patterns at this level, when something goes wrong, they can help correct it through genetic engineering.

For people from families that are prone to genetic diseases, scientists can insert a small amount of DNA material into a cell to interrupt the disease process. This interruption causes the immune system to recognize the cell as bad and destroy the diseased cell. This technique is still very new and used only in experiments. It will only be a few years before these techniques are widely available.

Human Genome Project — a project in which all human DNA sequences were mapped

DNA Mapping—Electrophoresis

DNA, like all molecules, has certain types of bonds holding it together. Each bond type can be cut by using chemicals. In the process of electrophoresis, DNA is cut into pieces. These pieces are then put into a liquid and a small electrical current is passed through it. Each piece of DNA material has a small charge on it, so it is attracted to the opposite charge on the other side of the liquid. The size of the DNA piece will limit its speed of travel through the solution. Smaller pieces move faster and farther; larger ones do not move as far.

This method is called electrophoresis and is used to identify the DNA sequences in organisms. Each individual of a species has different DNA sequences.

If a criminal leaves a hair from his head at a crime scene, a scientist can take the DNA off the hair cell and determine the exact number and types of DNA pieces present. Each person in the world has their own pattern of DNA, but families of people have some common DNA. This makes the technique useful to determine family heritage. Even if a person has been dead for years and a hair sample is found for that person, a positive DNA match can be made when using electrophoresis.

Electrophoresis — migration of electrically-charged DNA fragments in solution

NOTES

Recombinant DNA engineering can change characteristics.

There is a definite possibility that even DNA from prehistoric plants and animals may be isolated and examined. When these new DNA sequences are put into a chicken egg and grown, the phenotype or characteristic can be produced. If scientists can read the fossilized DNA, then they can engineer new DNA. Currently, recombinant DNA implanting is carried out to produce new or stronger characteristics in plants and animals.

Ethical problems exist at present in how far researchers are allowed to go in designing plant and animal life. Long–term studies have not occurred because these techniques are so new. The applications of genetic engineering are vast; however, the potential for negative consequences exists and so, society must be responsible in using genetic engineering many governments have enacted laws limiting the use of genetic engineering; for example, in Canada, scientists are only allowed to create cloned cells for medical and research purposes.

PRACTICE EXERCISE

1. Genotypes refer to
   A) physical characteristics
   B) amino acid sequences
   C) plant leaf shapes
   D) animal hair colour

2. Is it possible to cut DNA strands with a knife? Explain.

3. Explain how scientists could genetically map the DNA of a pea plant.

4. Humans have 23 chromosomes. How many genes do we have?

5. Design an experiment that will demonstrate that DNA is made up of different genes.
   Hypothesis: DNA is made of genes (amino acid sequences that can be identified).
   Method: Choose chemicals that will safely break the amino acid bonds at specific places.
   Use electrophoresis to pull them apart and then stain them.

6. Draw and label all of the stages of mitosis.

Lesson 5   CELL COMMUNICATION

Intercellular Open Communication

Cells working together form an open system where energy and materials are transferred between cells.

In multicellular life forms, cells working together to perform a task are called a tissue. It is very important for all cells in a tissue to work together. They are coordinated in their role because they can communicate with one another. Chemical messengers are sent between cells in tissues, organs, and organ systems.

The balancing of all of these systems must be constant for life to continue. Systems rely on each other to keep nutrients coming, remove waste, replace damaged cells, and keep temperature constant. This balance is called homeostasis and can only be maintained by these messenger molecules.

Medical researchers can now attach small coloured markers to these messengers and watch them cross a membrane. They observe how it happens and where the communication network goes. Scientists can label a hair cell messenger in the ear and watch the chemical travel into the brain areas responsible for sensory perception. In addition, with the aid of Scanning Tunneling Microscopes (STMs), Atomic Force Microscopes (AFMs), X-ray crystallography, and Green Fluorescent Protein (GFP) technology, scientists can see the actual shape of these messengers. This allows scientists to design effective drugs to help cells survive in our changing world.

Intercellular messengers are sent directly across into neighbouring cells. They are also sent via intercellular fluid to cells within the same tissue and organ. But, to get a message to another system or organ, the body's lymph and blood systems must be used.

NOTES

Cell Communication:

Intracellular — within the cell

Intercellular — between cells

Tissue — similar cells working together for one task

Organs — formed from tissue

Homeostasis: balance between nutrient supply, waste removal, cell replacement, and constant temperature

---

Intracellular Communication/Movement

Inside of all cells is a clear fluid called cytoplasm. All of the organelles float in the cytoplasm. To get nutrients and hormones from one part of a cell to another, the cytoplasm forms a stream.

Inside of single cells, molecules are produced in the ribosomes using ATP (adenosine triphosphate) energy produced in the mitochondria. Molecules and ions naturally diffuse through the cell membrane, but cytoplasm is often streamed from one side of the cell to the other. This not only brings molecules to where they are needed, but aids in cell movement.

Amoeba stream fluid from one part of the cell to another to be able to move. Once an amoeba has located food, chemical sensors alter membranes that change ion concentrations in one area of the cell. Fluid then flows in this direction because of the concentration gradient which results in the movement.

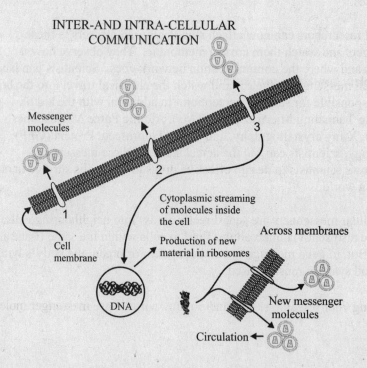

INTER-AND INTRA-CELLULAR COMMUNICATION

Messenger molecules

Cell membrane

1

2

3

Cytoplasmic streaming of molecules inside the cell

Production of new material in ribosomes

Across membranes

DNA

New messenger molecules

Circulation ←

The balance called homeostasis is required for all life to continue in a cell. All needs must be met in the correct proportions and timing for homeostasis to occur. DNA controls this process in addition to signals from our environment. Each part of the cell and the organism plays a vital role in maintaining homeostasis. Without an efficient open system, this would not be possible.

PRACTICE EXERCISE

1. Cells communicate through

   A) Talking   B) Mitosis

   C) Meiosis   D) Messengers

2. How can messenger molecules aid in homeostasis? On a cellular and on a system basis? Give an example of each.

3. Explain how cytoplasm streams.

4. Using your research skills, find out how viruses use messenger molecules to infect cells.

Lesson 6   CELL STRUCTURE

Animal Cell Organelles:
- cell membrane
- nucleus
- cytoplasm
- ribosomes
- lysosomes
- Golgi apparatus
- mitochondria
- endoplasmic reticulum
- vacuoles

Plant Cell Organelles:
- all of the above
- chloroplasts
- walls

All of the activity of a cell occurs in structures in the cell called *organelles*. The organelles of a typical animal cell are given below.

Cell membrane — for protection, support, selection transportation, and communication with other cells

Nucleus — for DNA storage and reproduction

Cytoplasm — a fluid that contains the cell's nutrients, controls their flow, and supports all internal organelles

Ribosomes — the site for protein manufacture in a cell, located near the endoplasmic reticulum

Lysosomes — a vacuole of wastes and digestive enzymes; bursts when a cell dies

Golgi apparatus — the site where proteins and lipids from the endoplasmic reticulum (see below) are modified and packaged for distribution

Mitochondria — the site for energy production (ATP) in the cell (cellular respiration)

Endoplasmic Reticulum (ER) — a tubular system inside the cell that circulates large molecules; Rough ER is surrounded by ribosomes making the channels appear rough; Smooth ER has no ribosomes around it but still moves molecules around

Vacuoles — membrane-covered sacs used to store materials, usually nutrients, wastes, or water

Plant cells have all of the organelles above, as well as:

Chloroplasts — small discs where photosynthesis occurs in cells

Walls — made of heavy concentrations of cellulose for firm support and structure

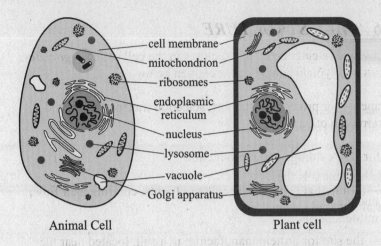

Animal Cell   Plant cell

The Carbon Cycle

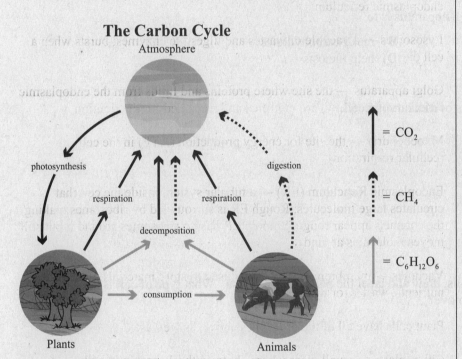

Atmosphere

photosynthesis

respiration   respiration

decomposition

consumption

Plants   Animals

digestion

= CO_2

= CH_4

= $C_6H_{12}O_6$

Since carbon is necessary for life to continue on earth, it must constantly cycle through nature.

Plants use carbon dioxide (CO_2) to produce a simple sugar called glucose. This sugar is consumed and the energy stored in the chemical bonds is released. Aerobic respiration in cells uses glucose and oxygen (O_2) to produce water and carbon dioxide. The energy released in this reaction is captured by adenosine diphosphate (ADP), which then adds another phosphate to form adenosine triphosphate (ATP).

$$C_6H_{12}O_6 + 6O_2 \rightarrow 6CO_2 + 6H_2O + ATP \text{ (energy)}$$

PRACTICE EXERCISE

1. Large vacuoles are present in

   A) plant cells   **B)** animal cells
   C) prokaryotes   **D)** all eukaryotes

2. When an organism dies, the first organelle to burst is the

   A) membrane   **B)** nucleus
   C) lysosome   **D)** mitochondria

3. The purpose of the Golgi apparatus is to

   A) make new proteins   **B)** make carbohydrates
   C) make fats   **D)** help meiosis

4. Draw and label the parts of a eukaryotic cell.

5. Using your research skills, draw and label the parts of an amoeba. What type of cell is this? How does the amoeba move?

6. Draw and label the carbon cycle.

7. Write the chemical equation for aerobic respiration.

Lesson 7   FLUID MOSAIC MODEL

Cells are made of lipids, carbohydrates, proteins, trace elements, and water.

Cell Composition

All cells have many common molecules and elements. The main ones are listed below.

- Lipids — fats and oils that make up the majority of the membranes in animal cells

- Carbohydrates — sugars and starches that make up the receptor molecules on cell membranes

- Proteins — amino acids and other building blocks such as DNA and membrane proteins

- Trace Elements — minerals, vitamins, elements, such as K^+, Na^+, Mg^{2+}, Li, Fe, and Ca

- Water — forms the majority of the cytoplasm

Each of these molecules and elements must be present in the correct amount or the cellular processes will either slow down or stop. Homeostasis is vital for a long healthy life. Death is a natural process, but it can be speeded up by lack of proper nutrients in the proper proportions. For example, if a person eliminates vitamin C from his or her diet by accident, then scurvy results. If cells lack anti-oxidants such as vitamins C, E, A, etc., then death slowly begins; whereas, the cell has all it needs, it will live out a normal life. Blood cells (red) will live for three weeks, but nerve cells can live for a lifetime. Isolated animal cells have been kept alive in a dish for over 40 years with the correct levels of nutrients.

Cell Membranes

To control cellular balance, an effective cell membrane must be in place to protect and preserve the cell contents. Membranes contain phospholipid molecules lined up tail-to-tail. The outer part is a phosphate head attached to a lipid or fatty acid tail. The tails of two lipids face each other in the centre of the membrane. Proteins float throughout the membrane as seen in the diagram below.

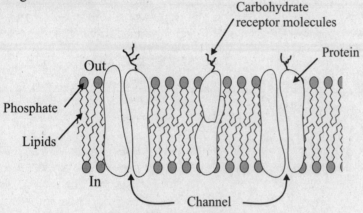

Fluid Mosaic Model of Cell Membrane

Fluid Mosaic Model —
proteins floating in
jelly-like fluid

Fluid Mosaic Model

The membrane is much like a jelly with protein molecules floating around inside of it. This model, verified by electron microscope images and chemical studies, is called the fluid mosaic model. The membrane is a double-layered phospholipid boundary that protects and isolates the cell. The proteins floating in the membrane have many functions.
Some of these proteins have hollow tubes through them that allow molecules and atoms into the cell. Some have twisted hollow tubes that open wide when a messenger molecule arrives. Nerve cell dendrites have many of these channels.

The proteins on the membrane surface can also have small carbohydrate chains on them. These act as receptors for the messenger molecules. Each has a very specific charge (polarity) and shape so that only the correct message will cause the channel to open.

PRACTICE EXERCISE

1. Draw and label the fluid mosaic model of the cell membrane.

2. What do carbohydrate chains on the outside of a cell membrane act as?

3. If the membrane is a fluid, how can it prevent water from leaving the cell?

4. Using your research skills, find out why insulin is necessary for normal cellular life. Explain.

Lesson 8   MOVEMENT ACROSS MEMBRANES

When molecules are too big or are not soluble in the membrane, the membrane must use energy to move the molecules through.

There are several ways to get the molecules through if the cell needs them. They include:

- concentration gradients
- passive transport/diffusion
- osmosis
- selective permeability
- facilitated diffusion
- active transport
- exocytosis/endocytosis

Concentration Gradients

All the processes of membrane transport act in response to a concentration gradient. A concentration gradient occurs when the amount of a substance outside the cell does not equal the amount inside the cell. When there is a difference in amount, molecules will try to move across the membrane to balance the concentrations. Water is one of the few molecules that can actually pass through a membrane without help. All other molecules need help. Both diffusion and osmosis occur as a result of concentration gradients.

When the concentration gradient is greater outside the cell than inside, the environment around the cell is hypertonic. When the environment around the cell has a lower concentration gradient, it is hypotonic.

When the concentration gradients are equal, the environment is isotonic.

To help get substances in and out of the cell without using energy, the cell uses both osmosis and diffusion.

Most membrane transport occur as a result of concentration and gradients.

Hypertonic: out > in
Hypotonic: out < in
Isotonic: out = in

NOTES

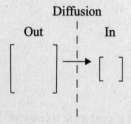

Hypertonic: out > in
Hypotonic: out < in
Isotonic: out = in

Passive Transport / Diffusion

When the concentration of an ion or molecule is higher outside the cell than inside the cell and the molecule can fit through the membrane, the chemical will move inside the cell to try and balance the concentration. For example, if the concentration of Na^+ ions outside of a nerve cell increases, the inside of the cell will respond by absorbing more sodium. The difference in ion concentrations across the membrane is called the concentration gradient. Water is a substance that diffuses easily across the membrane.

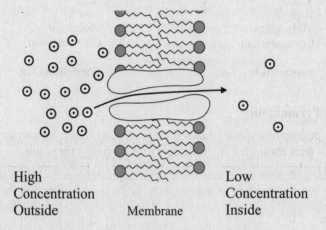

High
Concentration
Outside

Membrane

Low
Concentration
Inside

Osmosis

Osmosis occurs when a concentration gradient exists across a membrane but the ions cannot get through. In response, water molecules will diffuse across the membrane and balance the concentration gradient.

For example, if a raisin is left in a glass of water, in time, the raisin will swell as the higher concentration of electrolytes inside will draw the water in by the process of osmosis.

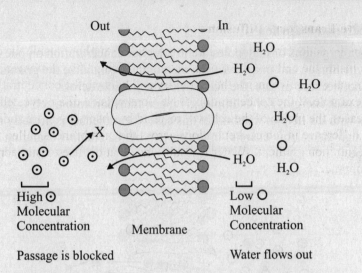

Osmosis

High ⊙
Molecular
Concentration

Membrane

Low ○
Molecular
Concentration

Passage is blocked

Water flows out

Selective Permeability

Selective permeability is a situation in which certain molecules or ions tare allowed to pass through a membrane while keeping others out.

For these molecules or ions, the membrane is said to be semi-permeable.

Quite often, the size of the pore in the membrane is a limiting factor.

The polarity of the molecule is also a factor because of the polarity of the membrane — like charges will repel each other. Some molecules will not dissolve in a phospholipid environment so they are repelled.

Therefore, only molecules with the correct size and charge can enter the cell in this way.

Selective permeability is determined by size and the polarity.

Selective
Permeability

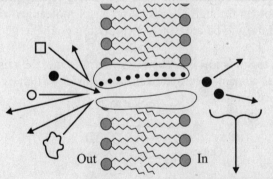

Out   In

The only molecules and ions that get through are the ones allowed

Facilitated Diffusion

When large ions or molecules are in a higher concentration on one side of the membrane and must cross the membrane to equalize the gradient but cannot because of size, the cell carries the particle across.

This uses energy. For example, glycogen transport into a cell is done this way with the help of insulin. In this case, the molecule is actually moved through the narrow channel in the protein by the channel changing its shape.

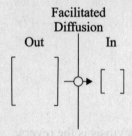

Facilitated
Diffusion

Out   In

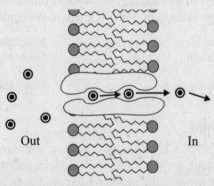

A protein changes the shape of the channel
so that the molecule can move through

Active Transport

Active transport is similar to facilitated diffusion, only it works against a concentration gradient. The cell pumps ions out of the cell in order to increase the concentration gradient. This is an energy-using process.

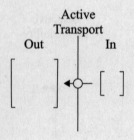

Active
Transport

Out   In

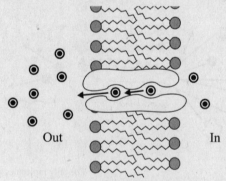

Ions are pumped out against
a concentration gradient

Exocytosis / Endocytosis

The process of exocytosis is where the cell expels chemicals (like hormones and neurotransmitters) in a cell-made vesicle.

Exo — out
Endo — in

The process of endocytosis occurs when a receptor molecule signals to the cell that a large molecule must enter the cell. The membrane then enfolds the molecule. The pouch pinches off and becomes a vesicle. The vesicle is moved to other areas of the cell. Viruses and bacteria may gain entrance to a cell in this manner if they can mimic the messenger configuration. Energy is used in both exocytosis and endocytosis.

Exocytosis is the reverse of endocytosis

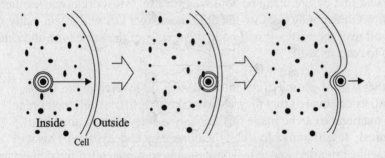

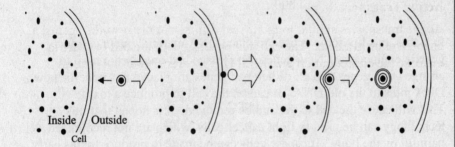

NOTES

Medical Considerations

Neuroscientists and cell biologists are experts at finding the shapes of the messenger molecules and the receptors in a cell membrane.
They spend years hunting for these keys and locks so that they can change the way a cell will work. They test different shapes and polarities and introduce them to the cells to find out if the cell will respond.
Once a cell does react, they can find out if it is the type of response that they want. This is one method of developing new medicines to ease suffering and cure diseases.

All drugs created have side-effects that can hurt patients. Each drug must be tested first before it can be approved for use. Most drugs cause other reactions in the body because the drug messenger key will affect many cells all over the body. It will go to other cells of the same type and cause them to react as well.

Another way of getting drugs into cells was discovered in the 1960s. Scientists discovered that they could make an artificial cell membrane. This membrane can be made tiny enough to carry a small amount of chemical. It will join onto a cell membrane by endocytosis. This will release the drug into the cell. These membranes are called liposomes and can be made as small as $\dfrac{1}{1\,000}$ of the diameter of a human hair.

In plants, this liposome is used to place DNA material into a cell for genetic engineering. New genes can replace bad ones or are used to change good genes to bad. When bad genes are placed in a cell, the new DNA joins to the old DNA. It causes the cell to produce a toxin.
This will cause the cell to die and be removed. It is hoped that this technology can be used to fight cancer cells, which are not recognized as harmful by the body. If cancer cells can be made to produce toxins early, they will be removed, thus preventing the cancer from growing.

Liposomes — artificial membrane

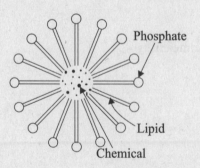

Phosphate

Lipid

Chemical

PRACTICE EXERCISE

1. Cells must be protected from the outside by membranes because

    A) concentration gradients will kill them

    B) cells must be able to select their function

    C) cellular life would stop if there were no difference in concentration gradients

    D) cells would die without nutrients

2. Draw a picture to explain each of the following processes:

    a) Passive diffusion

    b) Osmosis

    c) Selective permeability

    d) Facilitated diffusion

e) Active transport

f) Exocytosis

g) Endocytosis

3. Using your research skills, find out how neurons keep a resting potential. Explain.

4. What evidence is there that drugs can be designed to fit exact receptors on membranes?

Lesson 9 DIALYSIS

As cells live, they produce waste material called metabolic byproducts. If these chemicals build up inside the cell, it will die if the concentration gradients of these wastes are too high. In single-celled organisms, the cell simply releases the waste into the environment by exocytosis.
In multicellular organisms, these wastes must be eliminated by complex circulatory systems. They flush the wastes out while bringing in fresh nutrients.

In animals, the circulatory fluids are cleaned by the kidneys. Concentration gradients are used to flush excess ammonia and other molecules produced in the cells of an animal body. Diseases like diabetes, wear down the kidneys and they begin to fail. When this happens, the blood keeps its waste and the body suffers.

Scientists have devised two methods to rid the blood of waste for patients with impaired kidney function. These methods are called hemodialysis and peritoneal dialysis.

Hemodialysis

In hemodialysis the patient's blood is sent through a catheter (tube) to an instrument (artificial kidney) that which cleans the blood. The cleansing involves both osmosis and diffusion through a semipermeable artificial membrane. The patient must attend a health care facility to have this done frequently.

NOTES

Hemodialysis — cleansing blood outside the body

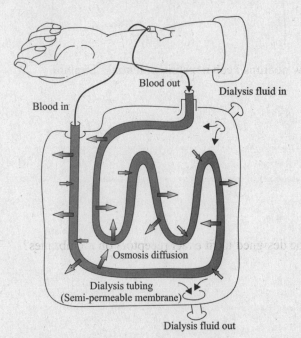

Blood out

Dialysis fluid in

Blood in

Osmosis diffusion

Dialysis tubing
(Semi-permeable membrane)

Dialysis fluid out

Peritoneal Dialysis — cleansing blood inside the body

Peritoneal Dialysis

In peritoneal dialysis, a tube is inserted into the patient's abdomen. A clean dialysis fluid containing proper amounts of sodium, potassium, magnesium, chlorine, calcium, glucose, and water is slowly pumped into the abdominal cavity from a bag carried on the hip. The lining of the abdominal cavity is a natural straining device for blood, so the waste diffuses out of the blood across the membrane while the nutrients diffuse the other way into the blood. After a few days, the abdominal fluid is pumped out and replaced. This method allows a patient to remain mobile.

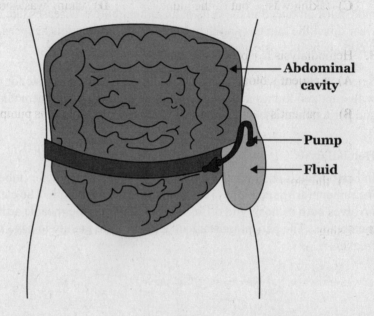

PRACTICE EXERCISE

1. Dialysis involves the processes of
   A) osmosis and diffusion
   B) diffusion and exocytosis
   C) active transport and excocytosis
   D) exocytosis and diffusion

2. Dialysis is a method of
   A) putting nutrients into the blood
   B) putting nutrients into the kidneys
   C) taking wastes out of the kidneys
   D) taking wastes out of the blood

3. Hemodialysis is a process in which
   A) a patient's blood is cleaned within the kidneys

   B) a patient's blood is drained while a donor's blood is pumped in

   C) clean dialysis fluid is pumped into the abdominal cavity

   D) the blood is filtered in an artificial kidney

4. Using your research skills, find and discuss ways to decrease kidney failure.

Lesson 10 MULTICELLULAR LIFE

NOTES

Small single-celled animals like amoeba survive quite well on their own in a good environment, though they have short life spans. Large cells have a problem as the needs of the cell far outweigh the ability of the cell membrane to transport enough nutrients and wastes for the cell.

Multicellular life forms must overcome all of the challenges of living together in order to grow and reproduce. Specialized cells handle specific duties and form tissues. Organs are formed from tissues that perform cleaning, communication, digestion, protection, movement, circulation and reproduction.

Yet with all of these special cell types, cells must remain small.
When an organism moves quickly to protect itself or catch food, cells require nutrients. This means they need more surface area to get more nutrients in and more wastes out faster. Cells that do not work at a fast pace are indirectly affected by the needs of other cells. The surface to volume ratio must remain high for a cell to survive.

Ratio Of Surface Area To Volume For Cubes

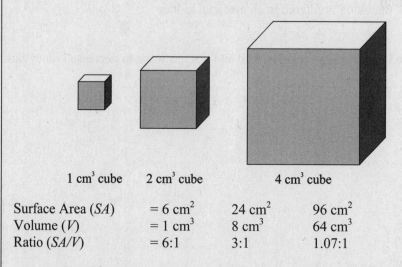

	1 cm³ cube	2 cm³ cube	4 cm³ cube
Surface Area (SA)	= 6 cm²	24 cm²	96 cm²
Volume (V)	= 1 cm³	8 cm³	64 cm³
Ratio (SA/V)	= 6:1	3:1	1.07:1

This comparison shows a dramatic SA/V ratio drop by a very small increase in cell size.

Multicellular organisms overcome the problem of getting nutrients to and wastes away from individual cells by having circulatory systems that come close to each cell. In a body with hundreds of millions of cells small capillaries in the blood stream bring fluids to within 0.1 mm of every cell. This is a very efficient system and can handle increased demands on the cell.

Cell Organization

Plants and animals have groups of cells that perform distinct roles or function. These groups of specialized cells are called tissues.
When a group of tissues performs a main function in one area, it is called an organ. In animals, a group of organs performing one main role, such as digestion is called a system.

Organ systems develop from the genetic material provided from one cell. This one cell is called a stem cell, which means that is an unspecialized cell that can reproduce into many different types of cells needed by the organism as it develops into an adult. For example, blood stem cells can turn into many different types of white blood cells as needed as the animal grows.

Cell shape is also role-dependent. Function determines structure.
For example, animal respiratory alveolar cells have a large surface area to allow for gas transfer across their membranes. Nerve cells can be up to a metre long to allow impulses to reach limbs quickly.

The division of labour in large organisms requires highly sophisticated cell communication in order to respond to external environmental fluctuations and stimuli.

PRACTICE EXERCISE

1. The brain is

   A) a tissue   **B)** an organ
   C) a system   **D)** a cell

2. What is the surface area of a spherical cell that has a diameter of 0.03 mm?

3. What is the volume of a blood cell with a diameter of 0.03 mm?

4. What is the surface area of a rectangular epithelial cell with side lengths of
   0.1 mm, 0.05 mm, and 0.08 mm?

5. What is the volume of the cell in question 4?

6. Does the cell in question 3 or question 4 have the best surface area–to–volume ratio?

7. Which cell, the one in question 3 or the one in question 4, would be able to survive better if the organism had to run hard for 5 km to get food? Explain.

8. Why is it better to have rectangular cells near the gut than round ones?

9. Determine the *SA/V* ratio for cell A, which has a diameter of 0.5 mm, and compare it to the *SA/V* ratio of cell B, which has a diameter of 2.0 cm.

10. Use your research skills to find some of the benefits of reintroducing stem cells into destroyed or diseased tissue.

11. Use the Internet to find the main argument against using stem cell in research or treatment.

12. Design a 100-cell animal and compare it to one that has 1 000 000 cells.
What extra has to be added to the larger organism?

Lesson 11 PLANTS

Plants, like animals, have tissues, organs, and systems. In plants, there are specialized leaf cells and reproductive organs that produce gametes such as pollen. There are only two organ systems in plants: the shoot system and the root system.

NOTES

Shoots — above ground and tubers
Roots — underground, except tubers

- Shoot system — This comprises all of the plant above the ground plus the swellings of the tubers (stems).

- Root system — This includes all of the underground tissue (excluding tubers) and any roots rising above ground.

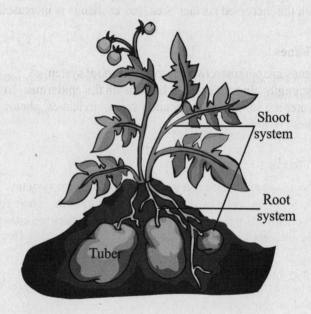

Shoot system

Root system

Tuber

PLANT TISSUE TYPES

Dermal / Epidermal Tissue

In the root system, the dermal tissue is the layer of cells covering all non-woody or herbaceous plants. Each layer is one cell thick which allows transport of molecules and ions (water and minerals) in and out of the plant. Woody plants have dead cork cells as an outer cover.

In the shoot system, dermal tissues protect the plants from the atmosphere and exchange gases with the air. Leaf dermal tissues secrete a waxy substance called cuticle. This is used to coat the leaf and prevent dehydration. The interior of leaves are loosely packed so air can circulate inside. With the increased surface area, gas exchange is increased.

Herbaceous plants — plants with little wood in their stems, survive for one growing season

Ground Tissues

Ground tissues are common to both root and shoot systems.
These are strengthening tissues that lie beneath the epidermis. In roots, the food and water are stored in the ground tissues. In leaves, photosynthesis occurs in these tissues.

Lignin — a chemical that glues cellulose together into cell walls

Vascular Tissues

The vascular tissues are common to both shoot and root systems.
They are thick-walled cells made of cellulose and lignin. Their function is to transport chemicals within the plant. Vascular tissues are either xylem or phloem.

Xylem — moves minerals and water

Xylem tissues move water and minerals to the leaves and stem.
As these cells mature, the ends thin and they die, leaving a straw for nutrients to flow through.

Phloem — moves sugar and water to storage area

Phloem tissues develop the same way. Phloem cells lose their nuclei as they mature. Around the outside of the cells are companion cells that keep their nuclei and control the movement of fluid in the phloem tubes. This circulatory tube is used for transporting the products of photosynthesis. They take the fluid sugars from the leaves to the tubers (like potatoes) and to the fruit of the plants.

Plant Vascular Tissues

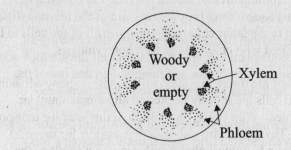

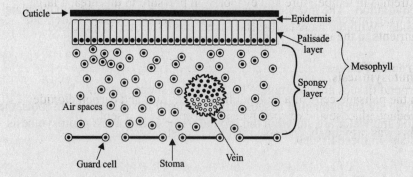

Leaf Structure

The veins of a leaf are the lines of vascular bundles that exist in the spongy mesophyll of the leaf interior. Xylem and phloem cells are present in the vascular bundles. They transport nutrients and fluids through the whole leaf. The veins extend from the leaves to the whole plant.

Growth Tissue

Meristem — plant stem cells

In animals and plants, stem cells are the precursor cells of all other tissues. As these cells grow and divide, they specialize into tissues. In plants, these stem cells are called meristem cells. Plant growth is constant in these areas but dormant in other areas. DNA is used in these cells to make the cells into the specialized cells needed at that location. The tip of roots and the tip of shoots are the growth areas in most plants.

Mesophyll Tissue

The area beneath the epidural area of leaves is called the mesophyll.
It is made up of the palisade tissues (upper one-third of the mesophyll) and is tightly packed with rectangular cells, which expose all of the cells to the air. These cells are filled with chloroplasts for photosynthesis.

The lower two-thirds of the tissue in a leaf is filled with a spongy-looking group of cells. These cells are loosely packed to allow maximum air circulation between them. The veins run through in this area for transport of sugars and water. These cells are also used for support for the most important function that a leaf does: photosynthesis. As a result of the extremes in temperature and evaporation pressure in this area, a large drawing power exists here. Here evaporation actually pulls water and nutrients to the leaves.

Photosynthesis

In the palisade cells of a leaf, sunlight plus water and carbon dioxide produce glucose and oxygen when chlorophyll is present.
This was previously discussed in the chemistry section.

$$6CO_2 + 6H_2O + photons \rightarrow C_6H_{12}O_6 + 6O_2$$

ATP — Energy source in cells

Light is absorbed by the chloroplasts of plant cells. The chemical chlorophyll is altered in the presence of light and reacts with CO_2 and water present in the chloroplast. The sugars produced are taken via the phloem to storage areas and altered into starches and storage sugars, unless needed immediately. The stored carbohydrate molecules are retrieved when needed and converted to an energy source called ATP in the mitochondria of the cells in a process called cellular respiration.

$$C_6H_{12}O_6 + 6O_2 \rightarrow 6CO_2 + 6H_2O + energy\ (ATP)$$

Cellular respiration is the exact reverse of photosynthesis and energy is released. The released ATP energy is then trapped in the mitochondria of the cell to be used by that cell for life processes.

During the day, plants produce sugars. At the same time, they use some of the sugars to produce ATP in cellular respiration. Photosynthesis uses carbon dioxide, while cellular respiration produces carbon dioxide.
The excess CO_2 is released from the cells and leaves into the atmosphere.
As the carbon dioxide concentration drops, the stomata close up.
The closing of the stomata preserves the internal gases and temperature of the leaf during the night.

NOTES

In plants, gas is released through the stoma openings between pairs of guard cells. If the guard cells detect an increase of CO_2 or light, they pull apart slightly creating an opening. This occurs because light stimulates the accumulation of K^+ ions in the cell through active transport.

This changes the concentration gradient and the osmotic pressure, which, in turn, draws water into the guard cells. The outer walls of the guard cells, that is the walls that are not touching each other, are thin and easily bulge as water intake causes the cells to enlarge. The bulging causes the guard cells to pull apart thereby causing an opening through which air passes into the spongy layer of the leaf.

Stoma size is determined by the amount of sunlight and CO_2.

Stoma close in dry weather.

When dry conditions prevail, water is lost as a result of evaporation through the stomata of the leaves and stems (lenticel cells).

Guard cells become limp as both water and K^+ decrease, causing the stomata to close. Plants in dry areas have fewer stomata in order to reduce water loss.

PRACTICE EXERCISE

1. Photosynthesis is a process that

   A) produces O_2 **B)** produces CO_2
   C) produces energy   **D)** can only occur in leaves

2. Cellular respiration is a process that

   A) uses CO_2 **B)** makes sugar
   C) produces energy   **D)** requires an open stoma

3. The opening of guard cells is triggered by an increase in

   A) CO   **B)** O_2
   C) sugar   **D)** light

4. When drought occurs what happens to a plant guard cell? What is the result?

5. Draw a diagram to explain the process of how a guard cell opens a stoma.

Lesson 12   PLANT TRANSPORTATION

Plants use four processes to move liquid within their systems:
- diffusion
- osmosis
- active transport
- transpiration

Water is drawn into the roots by diffusion. It is drawn into the phloem system by osmosis and transported up the xylem through the transpiration of water from the leaves. Other molecules are actively pumped into cells; for example, potassium is pumped into guard cells.

Water is a polar molecule: it has a small electrical charge on it.
Because of this charge, water molecules will stick to each other (cohesion) and will stick to cells close by (adhesion). These small attractive forces are what the plant relies on to get water all the way to the leaves.
In some plants, the leaves are over 100 m into the air. The water adheres to the walls of the xylem. It is pushed by the water diffusing into the roots and is drawn up the xylem straw by the evaporation in the upper parts of the plant.
This transpiration of water acts like a suction pump at the top of the plant.

Water is drawn up a plant by transpiration and pushed up by diffusion.

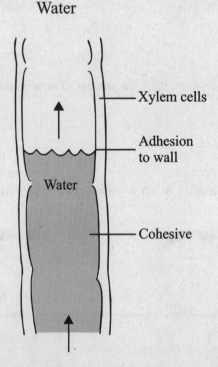

Water

Xylem cells

Adhesion to wall

Water

Cohesive

Large trees evaporate hundreds of litres of water a day into the atmosphere. As night draws near, the evaporation rate decreases, but since the roots are still absorbing water at a fast rate and the water is traveling up the stem, the roots push water up the plant. Water can travel up a stem at a rate of 75 cm/min.

Since water holds energy (remember the specific heat capacity and heat of vaporization of water), the presence of large quantities of water in a plant can save it from freezing overnight. If the temperature drops too low, the heat caught in the water will prevent the cells from freezing.
If the temperature stays low, the plant will eventually freeze but only after a large amount of energy has been given off into the atmosphere.

On a hot summer day, trees transpire large amounts of water from their leaves. This causes air to circulate near the tree. (You can actually feel a cool breeze if you are near the tree.) It takes a lot of energy to evaporate water. The air and sun supply the energy. Much of the world's thermal energy is stored in the various components of the hydrologic cycle, and plants play a large role in this cycle.

Plants provide a large portion of the evaporation within the hydrologic cycle.

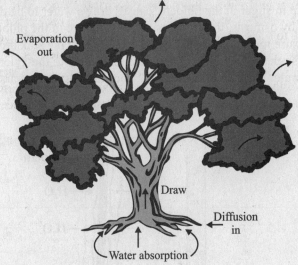

Evaporation out

Draw

Diffusion in

Water absorption

Turgidity

Large vacuoles take up space inside of plant cells.
These vacuoles normally have a pressure that pushes on the inside of the cell wall, keeping it rigid. When droughts occur, the water evaporates and the plants droop.

Plasmosis — ion pump causing water flow

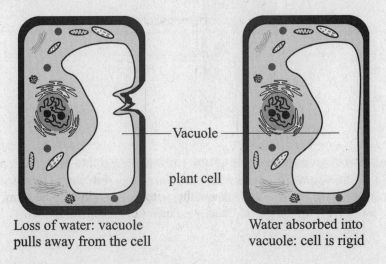

Vacuole

plant cell

Loss of water: vacuole pulls away from the cell

Water absorbed into vacuole: cell is rigid

Plant Movement

When turgidity is combined with a process called plasmosis, whereby plants pump ions into different cells, the concentration gradient increases and, water flows by osmosis into these target cells. With added water, cells become rigid which causes the plant to move in response to a stimulus. This is how a Venus fly trap moves its leaves to capture insects, and how plants move to follow the sunshine.

Pressure Flow Theory –
water comes in and pushes
fluid along phloem

Pressure Flow Theory

Plants send refined sugars and starches to be stored in tubers and fruits. The increase in sugar in the phloem, causes draws water to be drawn into the phloem by osmosis, thus increasing the pressure in the phloem. As the pressure increases, it pushes the sap down to the sink area. The water is released at the sink area and moves off to the xylem, which causes the water back up to the leaves. The starches and sugars move into the tubers.

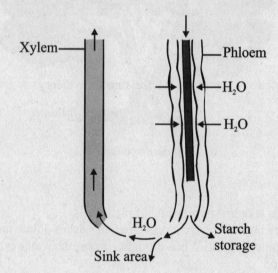

PRACTICE EXERCISE

1. Water can travel up a stem at a rate of

    A) 75 m/s   **B)** 75 cm/s
    C) 75 m/min   **D)** 75 cm/min

2. Turgidity means that a plant

    A) circulates water in the xylem   **B)** draws water up a stem quickly
    C) fills a vacuole   **D)** empties a vacuole

3. Explain the process of how a Venus–fly trap can catch a bug in its leaf.

4. Draw a detailed diagram of the pressure flow theory.

Lesson 13 PLANT DIRECTIONAL GROWTH

NOTES

Plants survive because they are able to grow toward nutrients and away from poor growth conditions. They do this by using

- phototropism
- gravitropism
- thermotropism
- chemotropism
- hydrotropism
- seasonal light variation

Phototropism –
+/– light response

Phototropism

Most plants grow toward sunlight, with the light (photo) being the stimulus and the movement (tropism) being the response. Stems and leaves normally have a positive reaction to light but roots grow in the opposite direction (negative phototropism). These observations have been understood for generations, but Peter Boysen-Jensen determined that it was the tip of the growing plant that responded to the light. The tip actually produces a hormone that triggers the growth.

Gravitropism
(Geotropism) – response to gravity.

Gravitropism (Geotropism)

Plant growth in response to gravity can also be positive or negative. Putting a plant on its side will result in the stem and leaves bending away (negative) from the earth and the roots turning to grow toward (positive) the earth's center. This growth is a result of the detected movement of large starch molecules at the bottom of cells. When the plant is moved, the starch molecules move as well. Plants in outer space do not respond as no movement of starch is detected.

Thermotropism

Plants will respond to changes in temperature as well as gravity and light. When a plant is warmed, it will continue to grow where it is warm. This is why some plants prefer being planted close to walls. If conditions are too hot, plants will grow away before they dry out and die.

Chemotropism

Plants grow toward areas with high concentrations of nutrients. Their roots detect these chemicals and branches are sent out toward the source. If unwanted chemicals are found close to some plants, they will send roots out in the opposite direction to avoid the chemicals.

Hydrotropism

Desert plants are famous for long root systems that grow great distances down to find water. Plants are able to grow toward soils with higher water concentrations. In swamps, plants actually send their roots up and out to find an area that has little water. In this way they spread across swampy areas, crossing from one dry patch to another.

Seasonal Exposure to Light

All plants respond to seasonal amounts of sunlight. If the season is not long enough, the plants will remain dormant until the following spring. Some plants are adapted for very short growing seasons like in the desert or in the arctic. Others will prosper only if the growing season is very long. Tropical plants are very sensitive to light exposure.

NOTES

Thermotropism — response to temperature change.

Chemotropism — response to nearby chemicals.

Hydrotropism —search for water.

Seasonal Light Exposure — response to differing amounts of sunlight.

PRACTICE EXERCISE

1. Gravitropism occurs as a result of the movement and location of

   A) starch in the cell   **B)** proteins in the cell
   C) lipids in the cell   **D)** minerals in the cell

2. Name six types of tropism.

3. Explain in detail how a plant responds to being shifted to a new location.

PRACTICE TEST

1. All eukaryotes have

   A) cell walls
   B) nuclei

2. Bacteria do not have

   A) cilia   **B)** nuclei
   C) vacuoles

3. Identify the organelles and the type of cell shown below.

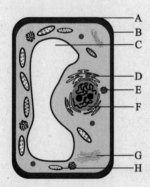

   A.   **B.**

   C.   **D.**

   E.   **F.**

   G.   **H.**

   Type of Cell:

4. The main difference between a plant cell and an animal cell is that a plant cell has a

   A) nuclear membrane   **B)** vacuoles
   C) cell walls   **D)** nucleus

5. Ribosomes are used for

   A) photosynthesis   **B)** respiration
   C) protein synthesis   **D)** circulation

6. The main site for cellular respiration in a cell is the

    A) mitochondria   **B)** chloroplasts
    C) vacuoles   **D)** Golgi apparatus

7. The types of the microscopes that can observe live cells are

    A) light and electron microscopes   **B)** light and confocal microscopes
    C) SEM and light microscopes   **D)** TEM and confocal microscopes

8. Louis Pasteur finally disproved the idea of

    A) tropisms   **B)** divine rule
    C) spontaneous generation

9. Given a low power magnification of 10×, a high power magnification of 100×, and a low power field of view of 3 mm, calculate the high power field of view.

10. Given a field of view of 0.3 mm and a red blood cell occupying 1/3 of the view,

    a) calculate the diameter of the red blood cell

    b) determine the magnification if the red blood cell is 1.5 mm.

11. How many genes are there in a human cell and how many chromosomes are there?

12. What sex do XY chromosomes indicate in humans?

13. STM is a _____ that allows the actual _____

of _____ to be seen with the eye.

14. Messenger and receptor molecules must combine correctly in which of the following manners?

- **A)** Shape and temperature
- **B)** Shape and polarity
- **C)** Temperature and polarity
- **D)** Movement and temperature

15. Phospholipids make up 80% of a

- **A)** nucleus
- **B)** mitochondria
- **C)** cell membrane

16. Cell walls are primarily made of

- **A)** proteins
- **B)** carbohydrates
- **C)** lipids

17. Which of the following methods is not used to transport ions/molecules across a membrane?

- **A)** Transpiration
- **B)** Osmosis
- **C)** Diffusion
- **D)** Facilitated diffusion

18. The most important principle in molecular/ion movement in cells is

- **A)** osmosis
- **B)** concentration gradient
- **C)** active transport

19. What is the process that releases most hormones into the blood?

20. Draw a liposome.

21. What is the main reason we do not have one-celled animals that measure 2 m across?

22. Define isotonic.

23. What will occur if you put red blood cells into a glass of water? Explain.

24. Write the complete balanced formula for photosynthesis.

25. Explain the Pressure Flow Theory of plants.

26. Draw and label the parts of a leaf.

27. Label the parts of the microscope.

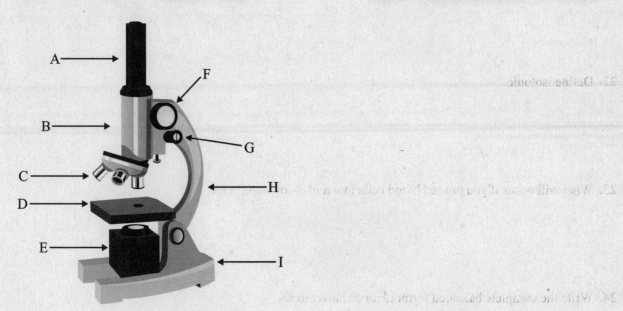

A.

B.

C.

D.

E.

F.

G.

H.

I.

NOTES

ENERGY FLOW IN GLOBAL SYSTEMS

When you are finished this unit, you will be able to explain…

- that energy from the sun sustains life on Earth through the life processes of plants.
- that energy from the sun sustains the life processes of the biosphere through photosynthesis and respiration.
- that the properties of water profoundly influence the nature of life on Earth.
- the measurement of water properties, the hydrologic cycle, winter aquatic survival and maintaining homeostasis.
- that the energy from the sun determines climate and drives weather systems.
- that the weather systems are driven indirectly by the sun's energy by air pressure, fronts and Coriolis Effects, and that climate is strongly affected by large bodies of water, currents, and latitudes.

223

Lesson 1   KINETIC MOLECULAR THEORY OF MATTER

The world around us can be better understood by knowing how each part of it works and how these parts interact. Particles in the atmosphere affect each other in many orderly ways. These patterns of interaction have been observed and written down. They were tested and are now known as the Kinetic Theory of Matter.

Kinetic Molecular Theory of Matter:

There are four main patterns that explain how small molecules and atoms act:

1. Atoms and molecules move

2. Increased temperature = increased movement

3. Increased movement = increased pressure

4. Increased distance = state changes

1. Atoms and molecules are always in motion.
2. Raising the temperature will increase the motion.
3. As the motion speeds up, the molecules press harder on the walls of the container they are in.
4. As the distance between molecules or atoms increases, the state of matter changes.

1. Molecules and atoms are in motion.

The only time molecules and atoms stop moving is when temperatures reach absolute zero. Quantitatively, absolute zero is represented by $0°K$ (Kelvin), which is $-273.15°C$. Molecules will bump up against each other on a random basis unless a direct pressure is exerted on them. Therefore, diffusion of molecules will take place randomly unless a force acts on these molecules to keep them together. The forces of nature cause patterns of movement to develop.

Molecules and atoms are always in motion

2. Raising the temperature increases motion.

If the temperature of water in a beaker is increased, the motion of the water molecules inside the beaker will increase. The water molecules pick up energy and move apart from each other.

Raising the temperature increases motion.

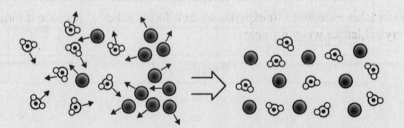

224

3. As motion increases, pressure increases.

When molecular motion is increased, a pressure is created that separates the molecules. A good example of this is when hot air is pumped into a hot-air balloon from a burner. The air begins to expand and fills up the balloon. The density of the air decreases and it causes the balloon to rise. If the temperature is kept high, the balloon rises higher; but if it cools, then the balloon begins to fall.

As motion increases, pressure is created that separates molecules.

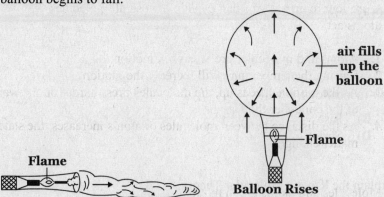

Flame

air fills up the balloon

Flame

Balloon Rises

4. As the distance between molecules or atoms increases, the state of matter changes from solid to liquid to gas.

When the distance between molecules increases, the volume and pressure increase. The state changes as this happens. The more heat you add, the farther apart the molecules will get. Solids turn to liquids and then to gases. Some elements like helium do this at very low temperatures. Others, like metals, do this at very high temperatures.

As distance between molecules or atoms increases, a change of state will occur

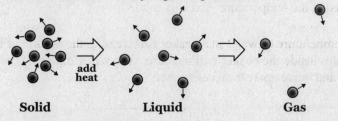

Solid   **add heat**   **Liquid**   **Gas**

Water is an exception: It expands when it forms solid ice because it forms a crystal lattice when it freezes.

PRACTICE EXERCISE

1. The first rule of the kinetic molecular theory states that atoms and molecules

    A)   Slow down as heat is applied

    B)   Change state as heat is applied

    C)   Separate as heat is taken away

    D)   Are always in motion

2. As gentle heat is added to the air in a balloon, it will

    A)   Sink   **B)**   Rise
    C)   Burst   **D)**   Shrink

3. In as few words as possible, explain the Kinetic Molecular Theory.

4. How does the energy of the sun directly affect the movement of air?

5. Using your research skills, find out why air rises at the equator and falls at about 23°N latitude.

Lesson 2   BIOMES

Weather patterns can be observed across all land masses on Earth. These are six major climate areas on Earth these are called biomes. Each biome has its own unique climate and plant life. Biomes can stretch over different continents, and the species of plants and animals vary in each. For example, the grazing animals in the taiga of Canada are not the same as those of the Russian taiga.

The six biomes are

1. Tundra: Mostly above 60°N latitude

2. Taiga: All above 30°N latitude

3. Deciduous Forests: Mostly above 20°N latitude

4. Grasslands: Between 60°N and 60°S latitude

5. Deserts: Between 40°N and 40°S latitude

6. Rainforests: Between 30°N and 30°S latitude

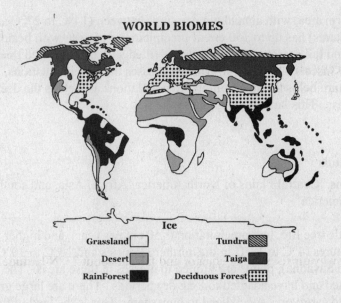

WORLD BIOMES

Ice

Grassland ☐   Tundra ▨

Desert ▦   Taiga ▪

RainForest ■   Deciduous Forest ▦

Tundra

Locations: Arctic areas

The average annual temperatures in these areas are between $-15°C$ and $5°C$. Short summers and little precipitation limit the plant life to lichens and shrubs. The animals are hardy but very limited in number. Many migratory birds nest in this area in the summer. This is the land of the caribou and polar bear.

Taiga

Locations: High altitudes and northern regions of North America and Asia

This area has cool annual temperatures ($4°C$ to $14°C$) with up to 100 cm of annual precipitation. The forests here are coniferous (cone bearing). The animal life is diverse ranging from moose and rabbits, to bears and eagles.

Deciduous Forests

Locations: Border grassland areas, eastern North America, Europe, Eastern Asia, and Japan.

This warm area, with annual temperatures between ($14°C$ to $27°C$ annual temperatures) has up to 150 cm of precipitation per year, with beautiful spring and fall seasons. The forests are filled with broad-leafed trees and mosses. Insects are plentiful, which increases the bird populations. This in turn helps the small omnivore populations as well as the deer and black bear. This land turns colour in the fall.

Grasslands

Locations: Central Plains of North America, Africa, Asia, and southern South America

With little tree life, low precipitation (<50 cm per year), and higher annual temperatures ($4°C$ to $18°C$ in the northern Prairies and $18°C$ to $30°C$ in the southern Savanna), plants are limited to grasses in these areas. The insects are limited and have adapted to long dry periods. There are large grazing herds and carnivores specialized to hunt them. This is the land of the buffalo and lions.

Rainforests

Locations: Tropics; areas around the equator

In these areas heavy rains (200 cm per year) and hot annual temperatures (25°C to 30°C) support all forms of plant and animal life.
From large snakes to insects as big as a plate, the variety of life in these areas is greatest of all of the biomes.

Deserts

Locations: Central Africa, Australia, Central and Western Asia, southwestern North America

In theses areas, average annual temperatures are from 12°C to 27°C, and less than 25 cm per year of rain limits the vegetation and animal life to those that can survive cold nights and hot days. This is the land of cactus, scorpions, camels, and roadrunners.

Canada has only four of the biomes, but we do have small areas with limited deserts (the badlands) and heavy rain forests (southern British Columbia coastline).

In the tundra, taiga, and deciduous forests, the lakes and rivers freeze in winter. Most insects and reptiles burrow into the mud at the bottom of the water. Temperatures remain steady under 4°C. The metabolisms of the animals slow down to decrease the need for food or gas exchanges.
Fish will migrate to deeper water and survive the winter on insect and plant life that has circulated down to lower depths.

Larger aquatic mammals will build lodges in the earth nearby or, like beavers, they will build lodges out of wood and mud. They venture into open water only to find food or retrieve stored food.

In grasslands and deserts, evaporation dries up the lakes in the dry seasons. Insects and reptiles burrow into the mud for survival. During the wet season, they flourish.

PRACTICE EXERCISE

1. List two specialized animals of the far north. How have they adapted to the climate?

2. Which biome has the most diverse life forms?

   A) Deciduous forests   **B)** Grasslands
   C) Rainforests   **D)** Taiga

3. The most dense tree foliage is found in the

   A) Coniferous forests   **B)** Deciduous forests
   C) Rainforests   **D)** Taiga

4. Name the four Canadian biomes.

5. On the world map below, show where the following biomes are located:

   a) Taiga   **b)** Grassland
   c) Rainforest

WORLD MAP

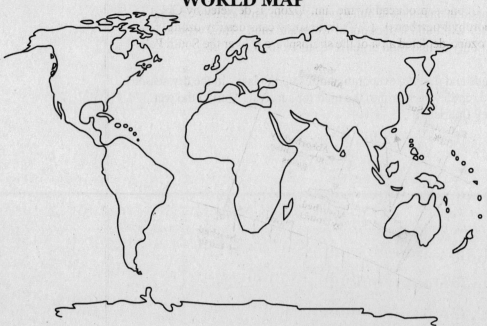

Lesson 3 *BIOSPHERE*

The area that sustains life on Earth is known as the biosphere.
There are three areas within the biosphere:

- Hydrosphere   (oceans, lakes, and water vapour)
- Lithosphere (Earth to a depth of about 85 km) and
- Atmosphere (the gaseous area above Earth) to 500 km.

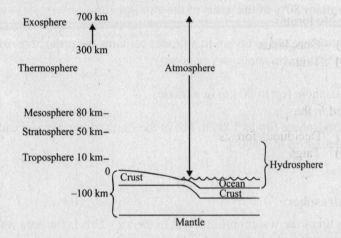

When the sun's energy waves and particles hit Earth, some energy, like
gamma rays, is reflected off parts of the atmosphere; some of the energy,
like neutrinos, passes through Earth; and some energy, like ultraviolet rays,
is absorbed by Earth.

Most ultraviolet light is reflected because of the ozone layer, which is
found in the stratosphere. Ultraviolet radiation causes cancer and kills
plankton. Ozone is produced by the sun. Ozone is depleted by CFCs
(chlorofluorohydrocarbons). CFCs from spray cans destroy ozone.
The most ozone-depleted area of the stratosphere is over the South Pole.

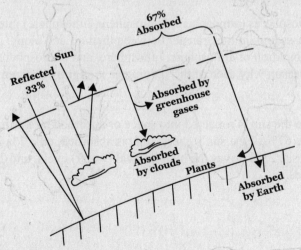

The Atmosphere

The atmosphere extends 300 km into space and is denser near Earth as gravity holds the nitrogen, $N_{2(g)}$ (80%), and oxygen, $O_{2(g)}$ (19%), close to the surface. Higher altitudes have temperatures as low as –100°C.

There are four layers to the atmosphere:

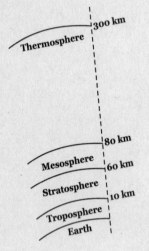

- Troposphere (up to 10 km in altitude), where life exists.
  It contains 80% of the gases of the atmosphere

- Stratosphere (up to 60 km in altitude) contains the protective ozone layer that gets warmer as you go up

- Mesosphere (up to 80 km in altitude)

- Thermosphere (up to 300 km above the Earth), here, the sun can heat molecules up to 1 500°C

The Hydrosphere

Contains all of the water on Earth and in the air. This is the area where heat energy is trapped. The hydrosphere prevents great changes in temperature on the surface of Earth. This area is heated by the sun which causes air and water currents. Because all organisms need water, life forms thrive in the hydrosphere.

The Lithosphere

The home of land animals and plants extends as deep as 100 km from Earth's surface. This mass of soil and rock floats on the mantle that covers Earth's liquid core. The deeper you go, the hotter it gets.

The three biospheres (atmosphere, hydrosphere, lithosphere) interact at all levels, as gases and liquids transfer between them. Each biome has a unique combination of atmosphere, lithosphere, and hydrosphere.
This is the reason why each of the six biomes is slightly different on each continent.

Energy from the sun is reflected into space or absorbed by Earth and things on it. Of the 67% of the sun's energy that is absorbed, only 1% is used for photosynthesis, 23% drives the hydrological (water) cycle, and 2% drives Earth's winds.

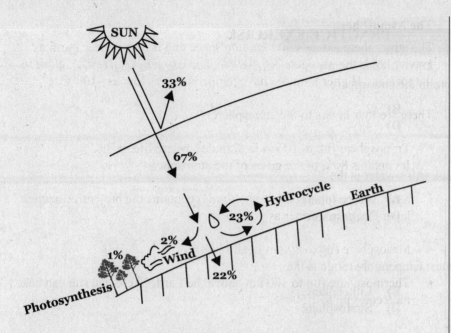

When energy is absorbed into the lithosphere, life forms known as autotrophs capture this energy by a process of photosynthesis.
In autotrophs, light is converted to chemical energy in the chloroplasts in cells. In the wall of the chloroplasts, photons of light cause a series of chemical reactions that result in chemical bonds being created.
It is within these bonds that energy is stored and transported around the plant in a molecule called ATP (adenosine triphosphate).
ATP is combined with water and oxygen to form carbohydrates.
The most common carbohydrate created by plants to store energy is glucose. Plants convert glucose molecules into various other sugars and starches to store the energy until it is needed.

Thus:
carbon dioxide + water + energy(sun) = glucose + oxygen

$$6CO_2 + 6H_2O + energy \rightarrow C_6H_{12}O_6 + 6O_2$$

Photosynthesis

$$6CO_2 + 6H_2O + energy \rightarrow$$
$$C_6H_{12}O_6 + 6O_2$$

PRACTICE EXERCISE

1. How many layers are there in the atmosphere?

   A) 1   **B)** 2
   C) 3   **D)** 4

2. The sphere containing all Earth's water is the

   A) Stratosphere   **B)** Troposphere
   C) Hydrosphere   **D)** Lithosphere

3. The sphere with the greatest temperature range is the

   A) Hydrosphere   **B)** Lithosphere
   C) Thermosphere   **D)** Stratosphere

4. List the two main gases of the atmosphere.

5. What percentage of the sun's energy is deflected from Earth?

   A) 22%   **B)** 23%
   C) 33%   **D)** 67%

6. In what way do the areas within the biosphere and radiation relate? Give one example.

7. The area of the biosphere on which all life forms live is called the _____.

8. The process of photosynthesis involves the conversion of gases and liquids to solids and gases by autotrophs. Explain.

Lesson 4   HETEROTROPHS

Plants and animals (heterotrophs) both use stored glucose molecules for their source of energy. Glucose is taken into cells and used in a process called cellular respiration. This takes place in the mitochondria of cells.

This chemical reaction is the reverse of photosynthesis because energy is released into the cell.

$$O_{2(g)} + C_6H_{12}O_{6(s)} \rightarrow CO_{2(g)} + H_2O_{(l)} + energy \ (ATP)$$

NOTES

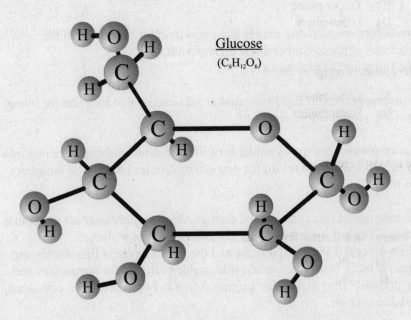

Glucose
($C_6H_{12}O_6$)

Glucose is burned in the mitochondria of all cells. It does not destroy the cell because the byproducts are removed and the energy is stored in a molecule called ATP or adenosine triphosphate. In the mitochondria, adenosine is combined with phosphate molecules that require energy to form the bonds. In this simple molecular form, the energy is now usable by the cell for life processes. The ATP is streamed to other areas of the cell to be used.

Energy storage and release is cycled, but these cycles are not 100% efficient. Energy is released accidentally from all processes, usually in the form of heat.

The other products of cellular respiration ($CO_{2(g)}$ and $H_2O_{(l)}$) are recycled. Producers like plants reuse both of these to make new glucose molecules. These glucose molecules are then eaten by a consumer.

They eventually end up being eaten by a decomposer. Some of the atoms are then reabsorbed by the producer as fertilizer. This conservation of matter on Earth forms a cycle as seen below.

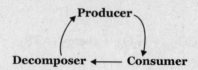

Producers create living matter from non-living matter through the processes of photosynthesis and chemosynthesis
(the formation of molecules).

Consumers convert this living matter into energy that they use for living (motion, reproduction, creation).

Decomposers take the byproducts of life and death and convert them into an energy source and return the original molecules back to the biosphere for reuse.

An example of this cycle can be seen in Alberta where deer eat the prairie grass. They are in turn eaten by carnivores such as wolves.

The wolves fall victim to disease and die. Decomposers like worms and bacteria break down the carcass into usable nutrients for themselves and the grasses. Thus molecules are transferred between producer, consumer, and decomposer.

PRACTICE EXERCISE

1. Give the chemical reaction for photosynthesis.

2. What is the main difference between cellular respiration and photosynthesis?

3. Energy released through cellular respiration is stored as

   A) DNA   B) ATP

   C) RNA   D) DTP

4. Using animals from the taiga, give an example of molecular recycling.

5. Given that plants and animals burn sugar to gain energy, why do the cells not burn up as well?

6. Give the chemical reaction for cellular respiration.

Lesson 5 SYSTEMS

Organisms work together within biospheres and biomes.
These separate organisms work together in systems.

There are three types of systems:

1. **Open systems** — where matter is exchanged with surroundings.
Animals and the plants they consume in the wild exchange matter and
energy and are therefore part of an open system.

2. **Closed systems** — where there is no exchange of matter, but energy is
exchanged with surroundings

Astronauts in a spacecraft exist in a closed system where only heat energy
is released into space by the firing of the spacecraft's engines.

3. **Isolated systems** — where there is no exchange of either matter or
energy with the surroundings

A totally isolated system can only be found in a sealed, isolated
experimental chamber where energy is not released or absorbed and where
matter is totally contained. Totally isolated systems do exist but they form
part of space environments on isolated bodies or on the inside of dormant
viruses.

It is often difficult to observe these systems in nature.

PRACTICE EXERCISE

1. List three examples of closed systems that humans are a part of.

2. Is a hermit living in a cave an open, a closed, or an isolated system? Explain.

3. Can an organism truly be part of an isolated system on this earth? Explain and justify your answer.

4. Design an open system using three levels of consumers and producers that are found in Alberta.

5. Describe how closed systems can exist inside an open system.

Lesson 6 *SPECIFIC HEAT CAPACITY OF WATER*

Weather and Climate

We know that solar heat warms all levels of the biosphere, but the heat is greater where the sun's rays hit Earth directly. The diagram below shows how the same amount of energy is spread over a greater area in the higher latitudes of Earth. Less dense energy means cooler temperatures.

These energy rays also hit Earth with a greater angle of incidence, thus reflecting more energy off Earth.

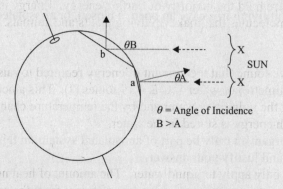

θ = Angle of Incidence
B > A

Heat, or thermal energy, causes changes in the air of the atmosphere. The heating of the molecules of the atmosphere causes them to move. The greater the heat, the more they move. These air movements form wind patterns on Earth. The circulatory wind patterns flow every 30° of latitude and create the main wind currents of Earth.

Coriolis Effect

The section of Earth causes these winds to bend slightly. This is called the Coriolis Effect and is shown on the diagram below as the bent wind lines at the equator.

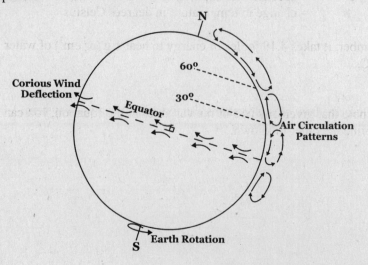

Specific Heat Capacity of Water

Water molecules have an ability to store large amounts of energy. The amount of energy carried by each molecule is called the Specific Heat Capacity of water. This heat capacity has a great impact on Earth's weather. Winds pick up evaporating water molecules and drop them in the form of precipitation.

Every time water evaporates, it absorbs energy. Every time water vapour condenses into rain or snow, it releases energy. Vast amounts of water in the hydrosphere hold the majority of Earth's energy. Energy is also stored in the water molecules that make up living plants and animals.

Scientists have found that the amount of energy required to raise 1 gram (or cubic centimetre) of water 1°C is 4.19 joules (J). This amount is multiplied by the volume of water and by the temperature change to find out how much energy is stored in the water.

These values only apply to liquid water. The amount of heat needed to change ice to water and water to vapour is different from the amount of energy needed to change the temperature of liquid water. It takes much more energy to change water to vapour than to change ice to water. It is important to know this because it directly affects the climate. Water has a way of stabilizing the climate and preventing large temperature changes.

Energy is calculated using the formula $Q = mc\Delta t$, where:

Q	= Energy in J
m	= mass of water in g
c	= specific heat capacity (for liquid water) of 4.19 J/g°C
Δt	= change in temperature in degrees Celsius

Remember, it takes 4.19 joules of energy to heat 1 g (or cm^3) of water by 1°C.

Also, note that given any two of the variables in the equation, you can determine the other unknown.

Energy:
$Q = mc\Delta t$

Example 1

Determine the energy required to heat 10.0 g of water at 0°C to 10.0°C.

Solution

$$Q = mc\Delta t$$
$$= (10 \text{ g})(4.19 \text{ J/g } °C)(10°C)$$
$$= 419 \text{ J}$$

Example 2

What amount of energy (Q) is required to increase the temperature of 10.0 g (10.0 ml) of water by 15.0°C?

Solution

$$Q = mc\Delta t$$
$$= (10 \text{ g})(4.19 \text{ J/g } °C)(15°C)$$
$$= 628.5 \text{ J}$$

PRACTICE EXERCISE

1. Determine the total energy needed to heat 1 L of water from 15°C to 98°C.
   (Hint: 1 L = 1 000 cm³)

2. What mass of water requires 1 000 J of energy to cause a temperature change of 50.0°C?

3. If 15 000 J of heat is applied to 3.00 kg of water, what will be the temperature change of the water?

4. If a body containing 50 kg of water is heated from 37°C to 40°C, what amount of energy was gained by the body?

5. If Q = 230 000 J and m = 4 000 g, what was the change in temperature that occurred?

6. If 400 J is added to 30.0 ml of water, by how many degrees Celsius will the temperature rise?

7. If the temperature of 4 200 ml of water rises 50.0°C, how much energy had to be added?

8. If a 40.0 L pot is heated with 5 000 J of energy, how hot will it get if the water is already at 20.0°C?

Lesson 7 WATER

Most living organisms are made up of at least 70–99% water. Homeostasis, or balance, is maintained in each cell to present it from dehydrating or exploding and in the whole organism so that it can function properly.

Remember that each gram of water can hold or release energy. Each gram has a specific heat capacity of 4.19 J/g°C.

Pure water has a melting point of 0°C and a vaporization point of 100°C. The melting point for most molecules is related to size, but water does not follow this pattern. Because the water molecule is made up of two hydrogen atoms and one oxygen atom, the bonds should be in line, but they are not. Extra electrons in the outer shell of the oxygen atom cause the bonds with hydrogen to bend at 105°C. The bend makes the oxygen side of the molecule more negative and the side with the hydrogen attached more positive.

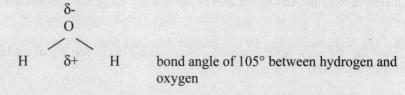

δ-
O

H δ+   H   bond angle of 105° between hydrogen and oxygen

The configuration seen above shows the slightly positive (δ+) H side and the slightly negative (δ-) O side of a water molecule. This is called polarity. Because the molecule is polar, it acts like a magnet with other charged particles(adhesion), including other water molecules(cohesion). (See the at-home lab.)

The attractive polarity causes water to adhere to the walls of tubes, such as xylem in plants, and allows water to be more easily drawn up.

In a drop of water, there are many molecules. There are small attractive cohesive forces between the hydrogen atoms of neighbouring water molecules. These attractive hydrogen bonds make it more difficult to freeze and to boil water as it takes more energy to separate the molecules.

Furthermore, the cohesion between water molecules causes droplet formation when there is no surface to adhere to, which is why rain falls in drops.

At-home lab:
Take a plastic strip (credit card) and rub it with a paper towel. At the kitchen sink, get a very thin stream of water flowing. Place the plastic near (not touching) the stream and notice the result

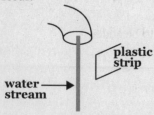

plastic strip

water stream

NOTES

Surface tension of water is also related to its configuration. When water is exposed to the air, the top layer of water simply inverts and fills into the spaces, as illustrated below. This doubles the density of the water at the surface. That is why it hurts when you slap water!

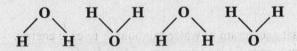

Ice, the frozen solid form of water, has a unique density.
When enough energy is released from liquid water, the H_2O molecules reconfigure into a six-sided crystal. This crystal takes up more space than liquid water. Because of this decrease in density, ice floats.
Interestingly, water is most dense at 4°C.

Heat Of Fusion/Vaporization

The amount of energy needed to change ice to water and water to vapour is different from the amount of energy needed to change the temperature of liquid water. There is no temperature change as the phase changes.

The heat of fusion is the amount of heat needed to convert 1 g of ice into 1 g of water at 0°C. It is a constant 333 J/g.

The heat of vaporization is the amount of energy required to turn 1 g of water to steam at 100°C. This is a constant 2 260 J/g.

To determine the energy needed to freeze, melt, condense, or vaporize water, use

$$Q = mH_f \quad \text{fusion}$$

$$Q = mH_v \quad \text{vaporization}$$

There is no temperature change as the phase changes.

Heat of Fusion (H_f)
= 333 J/g
Heat of Vaporization (H_v)
= 2 260 J/g

Phase change at a specific temperature,
Water = 0°C and 100°C

PRACTICE EXERCISE

1. How much energy is required to melt 100.0 g of ice?

2. Determine the total heat released when a 10 kg block of ice is melted.

3. How much energy does it take to vaporize 100 g of water?

4. When 1.0 kg of water vapour condenses, what is the total amount of energy released?

5. How much energy can be stored in 1.0 kg of water if the temperature is increased from 1.0° to 90°C?

6. How much energy would it take to melt 1.0 kg of ice at 0°C was melted and then heat it to 50°C?

7. How much energy is needed to vaporize 20 L of water?

8. If 450 J is added to 5.0 g of water at 99°C, is this enough to boil it?

Lesson 8 WATER AND WEATHER

Water has the ability to store incredible amounts of energy. Weather and climate are directly affected by this storage capacity because heated molecules move more. For example, a warm ocean current, has dramatic effects on nearby land. The Gulf Stream flows from the warm Caribbean Sea all the way across the Atlantic Ocean to the coast of Norway. This warm current prevents severe temperature changes near it but causes a far moister climate to prevail than if it were not close. This is why it rains so much in England.

Heat absorption causes air to circulate. As hot air rises, cool air mass takes its place. The movement of air over warm ocean currents and land creates regular wind patterns. The Lower Mainland of British Columbia typically has a daily onshore wind as a result of the fact that land heats faster than water. Soil absorbs heat faster than water. The warm air rises over land creating a low pressure area that draws cooler air in from the nearby ocean. This onshore breeze is also moist. It too heats and rises through the day, and clouds begin to form. The warmer air circulates out over the cooler ocean and then sinks back down to the ocean. This cyclic pattern is common on the west coast of North and South America.

Earth heats and cools faster than water.

HYDROLOGIC/TRANSPIRATION CYCLE

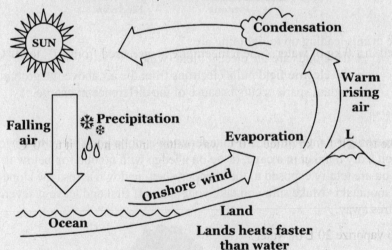

Hydrologic Cycle

In the evening, as the sun sets, the land begins to cool more rapidly than the water. This reverses the wind direction.

Given the considerable amount of heat gained by water when it evaporates and when it condenses, it is easy to understand that large amounts of heat are stored by water vapour. Large amounts of energy are also lost when it rains or snows.

Energy causes
thunderstorms

When this cycle occurs rapidly, storms develop, releasing incredible
amounts of energy. This release of energy caused by the consuming of the
water in the air results in a thunderstorm. This in turn causes the air to rise
even further, drawing up more moist air. With more moisture in the air
and a change in wind temperature at the end of the day, the water
precipitates out as rain. When the volume of water is large and the winds
are strong, massive energy changes eventually cause lightning to occur at
all levels. Lightning occurs as the circulation of wind and energy released
becomes so powerful that static charges build in the clouds. These charges
will flow, as do all electrical currents, toward the points of least resistance.

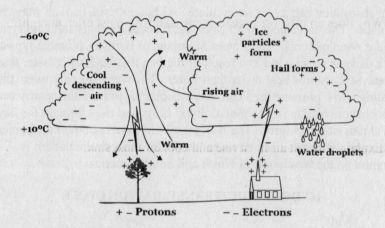

The events leading up to lightning are:
- the clouds are the electric field (wind)
- the electric field pulls electrons from the air above the ground
- a giant spark occurs because of the difference in charge

Remaining on a mountain in a thunderstorm is not a good idea unless you
sit on a dry blanket in a cave, or lie on a ledge with no outcrop below it.
If you are totally exposed to the weather, then lie down across the slope of
the mountain. Make sure you take your pack off first and leave it several
metres away.

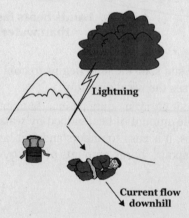

PRACTICE EXERCISE

1. Explain the process of energy release in a thunderstorm.
   Why does the energy not just transfer to the air?

2. Why does an offshore breeze occur, and why most often at night?

3. Explain why hot air must rise and cool air must sink.

4. Explain what specific heat capacity has to do with cloud development.

5. Describe in detail how a thunderstorm starts.

6. Why should you not climb mountains in a thunderstorm?

Lesson 9 AIR PRESSURES

Air pressure is measured in kilopascals or mm of Hg.

Air pressure refers to the amount of pressure exerted on Earth by the mass of molecules of air above it. Areas of high pressure have a larger number of molecules per square metre. They press down harder on Earth. When heat is added to air, the molecules move apart and rise. This decreases the pressure of the air on Earth. On a weather map, these pressure areas are marked with a large H (for high pressure) or L (for low pressure). Air pressure is measured in kilopascals or in millimetres of mercury.

Air moves from high to low pressure.

Air always moves as a mass from an area of high pressure to an area of low pressure. This is like a kitchen sink when you turn on the water. The high-pressure water comes out and pushes hard on the bottom of the sink. The water then slides down the low-pressure drain.

Warm front — rain

When a warm air mass hits a stationary cool air mass, the warm air mass rises up and slides over top of the cool air mass. This is called a warm front. This is represented on a weather map as a line with shaded half-circles on it.

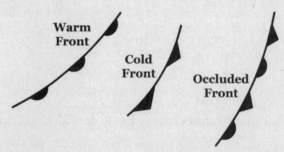

Cold front — cool weather

Occluded front — light rain

When a cool air mass hits a slower-moving warm air mass, it pushes its way under the warm air mass. This is called a cold front, which usually brings in cool and clear weather. This is represented on a map as a line with triangles on it.

Earth's rotation causes the Coriolis Effect and changes air pressure

Occluded fronts occur periodically as a slow-moving cold front overtakes a slower moving warm front. The result is a transition zone as a result of which produces clouds and light rain.

Air pressures are also affected by the rotation of Earth. As the earth rotates from west to east, the pressure changes as a result of the circulatory patterns developed. Recall that air pressure increases as air rises near the equator and at the 60° latitude lines and falls at both the 30° and 90° latitudes. The rotation of Earth bends these winds (the Coriolis Effect) and changes the air pressure of the winds. Severe storms develop in the low pressure areas and then move toward the poles. In the fall, in the Northern Hemisphere, these patterns produce hurricanes and severe storms over the oceans. They do great damage to population centres as they come close to land. When they hit land, the air heats and rises even faster, causing very destructive winds.

Added to this are the seasonal changes to air pressures that occur because of the heating patterns of the sun. When the rays of the sun directly (low angle of incidence) hit the low-pressure areas in the fall, extra energy is added to these hurricanes, driving them even faster.

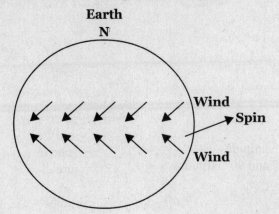

The arrows indicate wind direction.

PRACTICE EXERCISE

1. Explain how the Coriolis Effect starts.

2. Low pressure systems develop near the

   A) 0° latitude   B) 60° latitude
   C) 0° and 60° latitudes D) 30° and 90° latitudes

3. Occluded fronts normally produce

   A) Clear skies   B) Clouds and rain
   C) Hurricanes   D) No changes in weather

4. If Earth were to rotate in reverse, what would happen to our normal northwest winds? Explain.

5. Explain why winds in Alberta are predominantly from the northwest.

Lesson 10   WEATHER SYSTEMS

Hail

Hail forms when severe down drafts of air combine with precipitation in the form of rain. Hailstones (ice) form quickly in the fast-moving air and do not have a chance to thaw before hitting the ground. In fact, they build as they descend.

Tornadoes

When tornadoes develop, rapidly rising air spins in a counter-clockwise direction, creating a low pressure system. As the air speeds up, it decreases the air pressure even more. This causes the air to rise and spin even faster. This fast-moving air acts like a vacuum cleaner, drawing debris up into the funnel of air. The debris darkens the funnel giving a black look to it. The drawing power of these funnel clouds can pull houses off the ground and drop them long distances away.

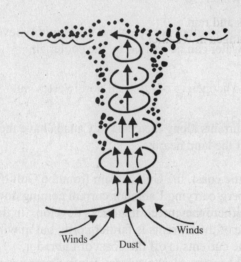

Winds   Winds
       Dust

Chinooks

In the area east of the Rocky Mountains, warm winter winds occasionally occur that melt all of the snow. These drastic alterations in weather actually begin on the Pacific Coast as warm wet, westerly winds.
The air rises and expands over the Coastal Mountains and precipitation falls as rain and snow depending on the elevation. The now dry air expands and rises as it hits the western slopes of the Rockies.
Any moisture still in the air precipitates out, releasing thermal energy into the atmosphere. As the air crosses the Rockies and begins to descend, the air pressure and temperature rise, forming a Chinook.

Air Masses in Canada

Canada has many common weather patterns as a result of the differences in terrain, the prevailing winds (air masses), and humidity (amount of water in the air).

- West of the Rocky Mountains, in British Columbia, the air is warmer and wetter, and comes from the Maritime Polar air mass.

- On the prairies, the wind blows constantly from the Continental Polar air mass and the air is dry.

- In central Canada, the winters are snowy and cold and the summers are warm and humid because of the moisture picked up by the northwest winds that blow over the many lakes in the north.

- In the east of Canada, the Gulf Stream warms the coastal areas in the summer and winter.

- In the north, the weather is cooler and the humidity levels are lower as not as much water can be carried by the cooler air.

Ocean Currents

Warm and cold currents along the coast of Canada have mediating effects on the climates of the land nearby.

- Off the Atlantic coast, the Gulf Stream from the Gulf of Mexico meets the cold, iceberg-carrying Labrador current coming down from Greenland. Where they meet, fog banks develop. In the summer, the meeting place of the currents is farther north, but in winter, the meeting of the currents is off the coast of Labrador.
- In the west, the warm Alaska current brings warm water to the coast of British Columbia.

PRACTICE EXERCISE

1. The name of the warm ocean current off the east coast of Canada is the

   A) Greenland current   B) Gulf Stream
   C) Labrador current   D) Alaska current

2. Tornadoes form as a result of the following conditions except

   A) Rapidly falling winds   B) Spiraling wind currents
   C) Rapidly rising currents   D) Decreasing air pressure

3. Chinooks originate from warm ocean currents and onshore winds that are heavy with water. Explain how these wet winds end up as clear warm air masses over Alberta in the winter.

4. How do fog banks develop?

5. Name the three ocean currents that affect Canadian climates.

Lesson 11 *RELATIVE HUMIDITY*

The amount of water that air can hold at sea level is dependent on the temperature of the air. The warmer the air is, the more water it can hold. This is called the humidity level.

Relative humidity is a comparison between the amount of water that the air is holding and the amount that it could hold. This comparison is done using two thermometers close to each other. One has a wet rag around it and the other is dry. Readings are taken from them and compared to a chart as seen below (the relative humidity chart).

Table of Relative Humidity in %

Dry Bulb Temperature in °C

		13	14.4	15.5	16.6	17.7	18.8
	3.3	7	2				
	4.4	15	11	7			
Wet Bulb	5.5	25	19	14	9	7	
in °C	6.6	34	29	22	17	13	8
	7.7	45	38	30	24	18	14
	8.8	55	47	40	33	26	21

If the wet temperature is 6.6°C and the dry temperature is 16.6°C, the relative humidity stands at 17%.

Dew point — the point at which water turns to liquid in the air

Air at lower temperatures holds less water. If a mass of air holding a lot of water cools quickly, the water will condense out as snow or rain or fog. The point at which the water turns to a liquid is called the dew point. At this temperature, the air is saturated with water and any cool surface nearby will cause water to condense on it. This is why dew forms on the grass in the morning.

PRACTICE EXERCISE

1. Using the chart on page 29, find the relative humidity

    a) If the outside temperature is 15.5°C and the wet temperature is 8.8°C.

    b) If the outside temperature is 16.6°C and the wet temperature is 5.5°C.

    c) If the outside temperature is 18.8°C and the wet temperature is 9.8°C.

2. Given a relative humidity of 25% and an outside temperature of 16.6°C, find the wet bulb temperature.

3. Given a relative humidity of 18% and a wet bulb temperature of 7.7°C, find the outside temperature.

4. Is the relative humidity of dry hot air greater or less than hot wet air? Explain.

5. Which of the following types of air would have the lowest dew point?
    A) Hot dry air   B) Cold dry air
    C) Hot moist air   D) Cold moist air

6. Explain your answer to question 5.

7. Why does cold air not hold as much water vapour as warm air?

Lesson 12   WEATHER PREDICTION

In Canada, meteorologists rely on many sources of information to predict the weather. They watch:

- humidity levels
- temperature changes
- pressure changes
- cloud levels
- wind patterns and speeds
- dew points
- precipitation levels
- radar images
- satellites images

There are two types of weather satellites above Canada: polar satellites and geostationary satellites. Each measures the amount of ultraviolet, visible, infrared, and microwave radiation in the atmosphere. Given the levels of these electromagnetic radiations, weather scientists are able to determine temperature, humidity, precipitation, ozone level, wind speed, and wind direction. They are also able to measure Earth's radiation budget, or the amount of radiation absorbed versus the amount reflected.
Radiation budgets affect wind patterns.

Satellites measure electromagnetic radiation.

Polar satellites circle Earth at an altitude of 700 – 200 km, every 100 minutes as they scan Earth. They orbit Earth completely, twice per day. Because these satellites are stationed relatively close to Earth, they can be directed quickly to any new weather pattern developing.

Geostationary satellites orbit slowly at an altitude of 35 790 km above the equator. They transmit the television weather photos back to Earth and give detailed images, which are updated every few moments.

On a national and local basis, Doppler radar is used to determine precipitation amounts and the direction of storms. Microwave pulses are sent out and they bounce off raindrops or ice crystals and return at a different frequency. If the frequency is less than the original, the precipitation is moving away from the station. If the frequency increases, the storm is moving toward the station.

Using all of the information provided, weather maps are then charted complete with isobars (air pressure measurements), temperature lines, and frontal lines to aid in determining a forecast.

Clouds

Weather predicting involves cloud identification. Condensed water in the air forms clouds. Cloud layers and types can be used to determine the temperature and speed of the air in the lower, middle, and upper atmosphere.

The cloud types are:

- Low-level clouds (below 2 000 m):
  Stratus, cumulus, nimbostratus, cumulonimbus
- Medium-level clouds (2 000 m – 6 800 m):
  Stratocumulus, altostratus, altocumulus
- High-level clouds (6 800 m – 15 250 m):
  Cirrocumulus, cirrostratus, cirrus

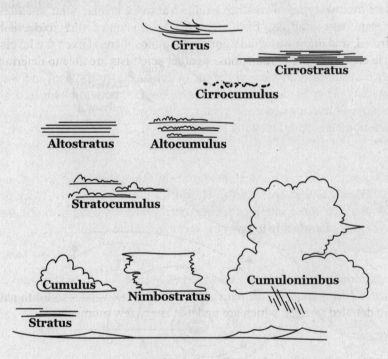

Weather maps have interesting symbols on them as seen below.

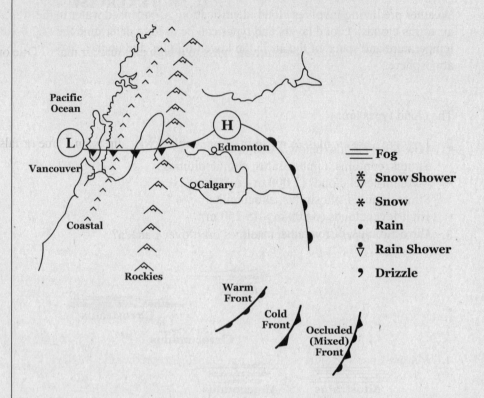

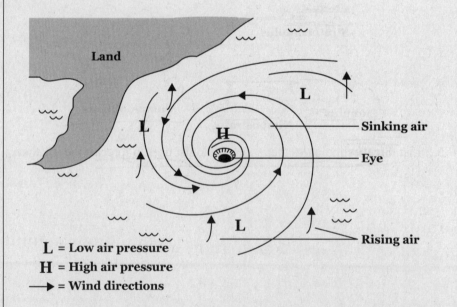

L = Low air pressure
H = High air pressure
→ = Wind directions

PRACTICE EXERCISE

1. Air moves from a low pressure air mass to a high pressure air mass. True or false?

2. Low pressure air masses move in a counterclockwise direction. True or false?

3. What two types of weather satellites orbit over Canada?

-
-

4. List four natural sources of information used to predict the weather.

-
-
-
-

5. List three technologies that a meteorologist uses to forecast the weather.

-
-
-

Use the following map to answer the next five questions.

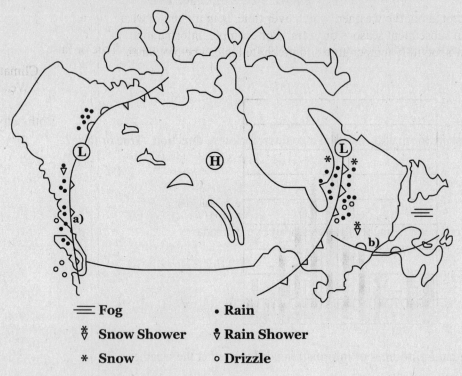

≡ **Fog**   • **Rain**

☇ **Snow Shower**   ꙮ **Rain Shower**

✻ **Snow**   ○ **Drizzle**

6. Using the map above, determine what part of Canada has the best weather for getting a tan.

7. Identify the areas where it is snowing.

8. Which direction are the pressure areas flowing from?

   a)

   b)

9. Explain why fog has developed in the Gulf of St. Lawrence.

10. Why is it raining on the coast of British Columbia?

11. Draw a weather map including a warm front, a cold front, and three forms of precipitation.

Lesson 13   CLIMATE GRAPHS

Records are kept about the weather, which over time, help to predict what may happen in subsequent seasons or years. For example, information about a region's monthly temperature and precipitation can be plotted as shown below.

NOTES

Climate — before
Weather — now

Both help predict the future.

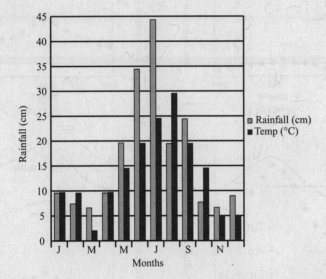

For this area, we can see that trends are clearly evident. This area is likely estimated in the medium latitudes because of higher but not extreme temperatures in July and August, and cold temperatures in winter.

It is also an area with a fair amount of rainfall all year and high rainfall in summer. This could represent the weather near the coast of a continent or downwind from a moist wind.

These graphs allow us to predict the amount of vegetation:
Warm wet summers would promote a lot of growth from April to October, a good growing season.

Each area of the world has its own climate graphs and, through comparison with biome data, we can pinpoint with a fair amount of certainty which part of the world the graph represents. For example:

- If the graph shows low rainfall amounts and high temperatures, it likely represents a desert.
- If the rainfall is increased just a bit, it represents the savanna.
- If temperatures were just a little lower, it would represent the prairies.
- If the temperature were even lower, the graph would represent the tundra.
- If the temperature and precipitation were raised, then it would represent the taiga.
- If the graph shows warm/hot temperatures all year long with a lot of rain, it likely represents a rainforest.

NOTES

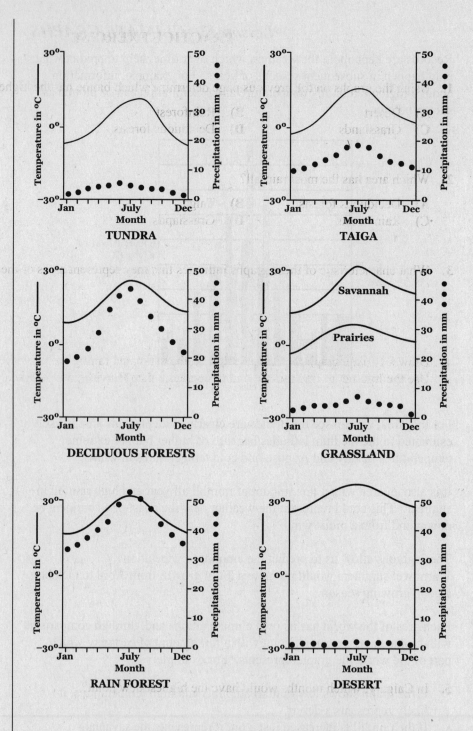

264

PRACTICE EXERCISE

1. Using the graphs on the previous page determine which biome has the highest temperatures.

   A) Desert
   B) Rainforest
   C) Grasslands
   D) Deciduous forests

2. Which area has the most rainfall?

   A) Deciduous forests
   B) Taiga
   C) Rainforests
   D) Grasslands

3. What characteristic of these graphs indicates that they represent areas of the Northern Hemisphere?

4. Draw a climate graph for Calgary. Put on the estimated rainfall and monthly temperatures.
   Use the Internet to find rainfall and temperature data (Environment Canada web site).

5. In Calgary, which months would have the highest dew point?

6. Which months are the best to visit Calgary if you like warm, dry weather?

PRACTICE TEST

1. Why does Earth's rotation cause winds?

2. Our main energy source is the _____.

3. What molecules are formed in photosynthesis?

   A) Carbon dioxide   **B)** Oxygen
   C) Glucose   **D)** Water

4. Cellular respiration produces carbon dioxide and water only. Is this statement true of false? Explain your answer.

5. Decomposers are organisms that eat other animals. True or false? Explain.

6. List three forms of energy that satellites are able to analyze.

   •

   •

   •

7. The amount of energy absorbed into the atmosphere from the sun is approximately

   A) 90%   **B)** 70%
   C) 30%   **D)** 15%

8. Ozone depletion results in an increase of _____ light getting through to the surface of Earth,

   causing _____ of the _____.

9. List three things we all can do to prevent the depletion of the ozone layer.

-

-

-

10. If 120 000.0 J of energy is applied to get 10.0 kg of water, what will be the temperature change?

11. The specific heat capacity of water helps to stabilize temperatures near the ocean. Why?

12. Why does ice float?

13. What substance dissolves chlorophyll out of a leaf?

   A) Water   **B)** Alcohol

   C) Ether   **D)** Pentane

14. The specific heat of vaporization of water is _____.

15. How much energy is required to change the temperature of 20 kg of water by 10°C?

16. Determine the additional amount of energy stored in 15 kg of water when the temperature is raised 10°C.

17. The units of measure for the heat of vaporization are _____.

18. Weather is a changing phenomenon that is dependent on a few important factors. Name three of them and explain why they are important in predicting weather.

-

-

-

19. In 5 steps, explain how a Chinook forms.

-

-

-

-

-

20. What are the four main principles of the Kinetic Molecular Theory of Matter?

-

-

-

-

21. What is a convection current?

22. The arctic has a period of the year when the sun does not set. Why can we not grow potatoes there?

23. If the relative humidity of an area is high, what does that indicate about the difference between wet and dry bulb temperatures for the area?

24. When a cool air mass hits a warm air mass, what occurs?

25. Clouds form when the _____ point is reached in moist air.

26. Tornadoes cause damage as a result of the extreme variations in _____.

27. Behind a warm front, what is the weather like?

28. On the coast, when someone says "red sky at night, sailor's delight" what does it mean in terms of the weather for the next day? Explain the cause of the red sky.

29. Draw a transpiration cycle.

30. Name one type of low cloud.

STUDENT NOTES AND PROBLEMS

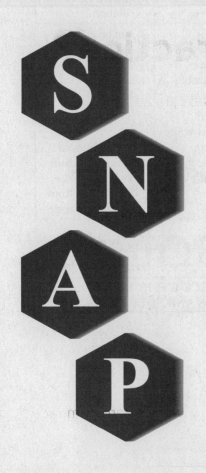

Answers
and
Solutions

ENERGY AND MATTER IN CHEMICAL CHANGE

Lesson 1—Matter

PRACTICE EXERCISE— ANSWERS AND SOLUTIONS

1.

Reaction	Physical	Chemical
Ice melts to water	✓	
Burning paper		✓
Making dry ice (solidification of carbon dioxide)	✓	
Cooking a hamburger		✓
Boiling water	✓	
Burning natural gas in a furnace		✓
Making wine by fermentation		✓
Boiling an egg		✓

3. • Solid
   • Gold colour
   • Conductive
   • Melting point 1 064°C

5. B

7. A

9.

Substance	Physical Properties	Chemical Properties
Carbon dioxide	– gas at room temp. – colorless – heavier than air – irritating odour	– neutralizes alkaline solutions – freezes to form dry ice – forms carbonic acid in solution
Copper	– metal – shiny, red colour – malleable – ductile	– can be alloyed – atomic number is 27 – acts as an oxidiser
Aluminum	– metal – silver-white colour – malleable – ductile	– atomic number is 13 – can be alloyed – several precious stones are formed from aluminum oxide

Lesson 2—Classification of Matter

PRACTICE EXERCISE— ANSWERS AND SOLUTIONS

1. Colloidal

3. Element

5. Solution

7. Suspension

9. D

11. Elements and compounds

Lesson 3—The Scientific Method

PRACTICE EXERCISE—
ANSWERS AND SOLUTIONS

1. **a)** 5
   b) 1
   c) 6
   d) 2
   e) 4
   f) 3

Lesson 4—Periodic Chart of the Elements

PRACTICE EXERCISE—
ANSWERS AND SOLUTIONS

1. • Metals
   • Nonmetals
   • Metalloids

3. • Physical – Soft
               – Shiny
               – Ductile
   • Chemical – forms a white crystal

5. **a)** Mg
   b) Cu
   c) S
   d) hydrogen
   e) lead
   f) calcium

7.

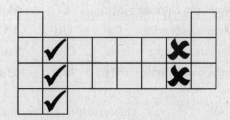

Lesson 5—Atoms

PRACTICE EXERCISE—
ANSWERS AND SOLUTIONS

1.

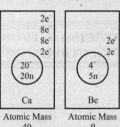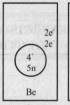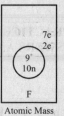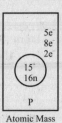

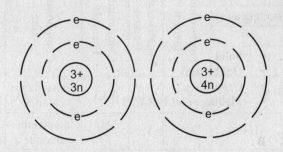

3. 1.7×10^{-24} g

5. **B**

7.

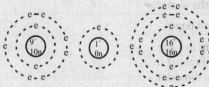

9.

Element	Period	Group
Ne	2	8
Al	3	3
N	2	5
Li	2	1
Cl	3	7
Ca	4	2
O	2	6
Be	2	2

Lesson 6—Ions

PRACTICE EXERCISE— ANSWERS AND SOLUTIONS

1.

Atom	Ion	Electron gain	Electron loss
O	O^{2-}	$2e^-$	
Li	Li^+		$1e^-$
Mg	Mg^{2+}		$2e^-$
F	F^-	$1e^-$	
Ca	Ca^{2+}		$2e^-$
Al	Al^{3+}		$3e^-$
N	N^{3-}	$3e^-$	

Lesson 7—Compounds

PRACTICE EXERCISE— ANSWERS AND SOLUTIONS

Elements	Positive ion formed	Negative ion formed	Compound Formula	Compound Name
K + Cl	K^+	Cl^-	KCl	potassium chloride
Al + F	Al^{3+}	F^-	AlF_3	aluminum fluoride
Li + O	Li^+	O^{2-}	Li_2O	lithium oxide
Be + N	Be^{2+}	N^{3-}	Be_3N_2	beryllium nitride
Na + O	Na^+	O^{2-}	Na_2O	sodium oxide
K + N	K^+	N^{3-}	K_3N	potassium nitride
Ca + Br	Ca^{2+}	Br^-	$CaBr_2$	calcium bromide
Mg + I	Mg^{2+}	I^-	MgI_2	magnesium iodide

Lesson 8—Ions with Multiple Charges

PRACTICE EXERCISE— ANSWERS AND SOLUTIONS

1.

Formula	Metal Ion Charge	Non-Metal Ion Charge	Name
$NiCl_3$	Ni^{3+}	Cl^-	Nickel (III) Chloride
MnO	Mn^{2+}	O^{2-}	Manganese (II) oxide
Cr_2O_3	Cr^{3+}	O^{2-}	Chromium (III) oxide
$CuCl_2$	Cu^{2+}	Cl^-	Copper (II) chloride
PbO_2	Pb^{4+}	O^{2-}	lead (IV) oxide
FeO	Fe^{2+}	O^{2-}	iron (II) oxide

Lesson 9—Polyatomic Ions

PRACTICE EXERCISE— ANSWERS AND SOLUTIONS

1.

Compound	Cation	Anion	Formula
Barium sulfate	Ba^{2+}	SO_4^{2-}	$BaSO_4$
Aluminum bromide	Al^{3+}	Br^-	$AlBr_3$
Zinc oxide	Zn^{2+}	O^{2-}	ZnO
Magnesium chloride	Mg^{2+}	Cl^-	$MgCl_2$
Calcium hydroxide	Ca^{2+}	OH^-	$Ca(OH)_2$
Sodium chlorate	Na^+	ClO_3^-	$NaClO_3$
Ammonium nitrate	NH_4^+	NO_3^-	NH_4NO_3

3. Any of chlorate, sulfate, sulfite, nitrate, nitrite, hydroxide, ammonium, phosphate, or carbonate

ClO_3^- SO_4^{2-} SO_3^{2-}
NO_3^- NO_2^- OH^-
NH_4^+ PO_4^{3-} CO_3^{2-}

Lesson 10—Molecular Compounds

PRACTICE EXERCISE—
ANSWERS AND SOLUTIONS

1. B

3.

H_2O	Water
CH_4	Methane
H_2O_2	Hydrogen peroxide
H_2S	Hydrogen sulfide
$C_6H_{12}O_6$	Glucose
CH_3OH	Methanol

5.

Formula	Name
SiO_2	Silicon dioxide
OCl_2	Oxygen dichloride
SO_3	Sulfur trioxide
CO_2	Carbon dioxide
NO_2	Nitrogen dioxide

Lesson 11—Properties of Ionic Compounds

PRACTICE EXERCISE—
ANSWERS AND SOLUTIONS

1.

Name	Formula	Solubility in Water
Sodium chloride	$NaCl$	Yes, all group I metals are soluble.
Silver nitrate	$AgNO_3$	Yes, all nitrates are soluble.
Magnesium sulfate	$MgSO_4$	Yes, most sulfates are soluble.
Aluminum chloride	$AlCl_3$	Yes, most chlorides are soluble.
Calcium sulfate	$CaSO_4$	No, Ca is not soluble with SO_4^{2-}
Beryllium hydroxide	$Be(OH)_2$	No, Be is not soluble in OH^-.
Sodium phosphate	Na_3PO_4	Yes, group IA elements are soluble in PO_4^{3-}
Lithium chlorate	$LiClO_3$	Yes, all ClO_3^- are soluble.

Lesson 12—States of Chemical Reactions

PRACTICE EXERCISE—
ANSWERS AND SOLUTIONS

1. $K_{(s)}$

3. $S_{8(s)}$

5. $NaCl_{(s)}$

7. $CH_{4(g)}$

Lesson 13—Acids and Bases

PRACTICE EXERCISE—
ANSWERS AND SOLUTIONS

1.

Acid Name	Binary or Oxy	Formula
Hydrobromic acid	Binary	$HBr_{(aq)}$
Sulfurous acid	Oxy	$H_2SO_{3(aq)}$
Hydrochloric acid	Binary	$HCl_{(aq)}$
Nitric acid	Oxy	$HNO_{3(aq)}$
Hydrofluoric acid	Binary	$HF_{(aq)}$
Nitrous acid	Oxy	$HNO_{2(aq)}$

3.

Formula	Compound Name	Acid, Base, Ionic, Molecular
$Ca(NO_3)_{2(s)}$	Calcium nitrate	Ionic compound
$H_2SO_{4(aq)}$	Sulfuric acid	Acid
$(NH_4)_2SO_{3(aq)}$	Ammonium sulfite	Ionic compound
$NaCl_{(aq)}$	Sodium chloride	Ionic compound
$P_2O_{5(g)}$	Diphosphorous pentoxide	Molecular compound
$KOH_{(aq)}$	Potassium hydroxide	Base

5. C

7. B

9. A

11. An acid with pH 2 is stronger than an acid with pH 5.

13.

Hydrochloric acid	$HCl_{(aq)}$	B
Nitric acid		O
Boric acid	H_3BO_3	O
Phosphoric acid		O
Sulfuric acid	$H_2SO_{4(aq)}$	O

Lesson 14—Chemical Equations

PRACTICE EXERCISE—
ANSWERS AND SOLUTIONS

1. **a)**

L.S.	R.S.
4Al	4Al
6O	6O

b)

L.S.	R.S.
2Cl	2Cl
2K	2K
2I	2I

c)

L.S.	R.S.
2N	2N
4H	4H
3O	3O

d)

L.S.	R.S.
6H	6H
3S	3S
20O	20O
3Ca	3Ca
2P	2P

Lesson 15—Chemical Reaction Types

PRACTICE EXERCISE—
ANSWERS AND SOLUTIONS

1. $C_{(s)} + O_{2(g)} \rightarrow CO_{2(g)}$

3. $4Fe_{(s)} + 3O_{2(g)} \rightarrow 2Fe_2O_{3(g)}$

5. $2FeO_{(s)} + heat \rightarrow 2Fe_{(s)} + O_{2(g)}$

7. $2Al_{(s)} + 3NaCl_{(aq)} \rightarrow 2AlCl3_{(aq)} + 3Na_{(s)}$

9. $Ca_{(s)} + 2LiOH_{(aq)} \rightarrow Ca(OH)_{2(aq)} + 2Li_{(s)}$

11. $KMnO_{4(aq)} + (NH_4)_2SO_{4(aq)}$
$\rightarrow K_2SO_{4(aq)} + NH_4MnO_{4(ag)}$

13. $C_3H_{8(g)} + 5O_{2(g)} \rightarrow 3CO_{2(g)} + 4H_2O_{(g)}$

15. $C_4H_{10(g)} + O_{2(g)} \rightarrow CO_{2(g)} + H_2O_{(l)}$

17. $2Fe + O_2 + 2H_2O \rightarrow 2Fe(OH)_2$

19. a) F $\quad N_{2(g)} + 2H_{2(g)} \rightarrow 2NH_{2(g)}$

b) F $\quad 2Na_{(s)} + Cl_{2(g)} \rightarrow 2NaCl_{(s)}$

c) SD $\quad 2H_2O_{(l)} \rightarrow 2H_{2(g)} + O_{2(g)}$

d) SR $\quad 2Na_{(s)} + 2H_2O_{(l)} \rightarrow 2NaOH_{(aq)} + H_{2(g)}$

e) SR $\quad Zn_{(s)} + 2HCl_{(aq)} \rightarrow ZnCl_{2(aq)} + H_{2(g)}$

f) C $\quad CH_{4(g)} + 2O_{2(g)} \rightarrow CO_{2(g)} + 2H_2O_{(g)}$

g) F $\quad P_{4(s)} + 10Cl_{2(g)} \rightarrow 4PCl_{5(s)}$

h) SR $\quad CoCl_{2(aq)} + 2Na_{(s)} \rightarrow 2NaCl_{(aq)} + Co_{(s)}$

i) DR $\quad 2Na_3PO_{4(aq)} + 3MgCl_{2(aq)} \rightarrow Mg_3(PO_4)_{2(s)} + 6NaCl_{(aq)}$

j) C $\quad 2C_4H_{10(g)} + 12O_{2(g)} \rightarrow 8CO_{2(g)} + 10H_2O_{(g)}$

k) SD $\quad 2P_2O_{5(s)} \rightarrow P_{4(s)} + 5O_{2(g)}$

l) SD $\quad 2Al_{(s)} + 3Cu(NO_2)_{2(aq)} \rightarrow 3Cu_{(s)} + 2Al(NO_2)_{3(aq)}$

m) DR $\quad CaC_{2(s)} + 2H_2O_{(l)} \rightarrow C_2H_{2(g)} + Ca(OH)_{2(s)}$

Lesson 16—Chemical Reaction Rates

PRACTICE EXERCISE— ANSWERS AND SOLUTIONS

1. B

3. When the surface area of the reactants is increased, the rate of the reaction also increases.

Lesson 17—Moles

PRACTICE EXERCISE— ANSWERS AND SOLUTIONS

1.

Formula	Name	Molar Mass (g/mol)
$Na_2SO_{4(s)}$	sodium sulfate	Na – $22.99 \times 2 = 45.98$ S – $32.06 \times 1 = 32.06$ O – $16.00 \times 4 = \underline{64.00}$ molar mass = 142.04
$Ca(NO_3)_{2(s)}$	calcium nitrate	Ca – $40 \times 1 = 40.00$ N – $14 \times 2 = 28.00$ O – $16 \times 6 = \underline{96.00}$ molar mass = 164.00
$N_2O_{5(g)}$	dinitrogen pentoxide	N – $14 \times 2 = 20.00$ O – $16 \times 5 = \underline{80.00}$ molar mass = 164.00
$K_2Cr_2O_{7(s)}$	potassium dichromate	K – $39.10 \times 2 = 78.20$ Cr – $52.00 \times 2 = 104.00$ O – $16.00 \times 7 = \underline{112.00}$ molar mass = 294.20
$Al_2O_{3(s)}$	aluminum oxide	Al – $27 \times 2 = 54.00$ O – $16 \times 3 = \underline{48.00}$ molar mass = 132.00
$(NH_4)_2SO_{4(s)}$	ammonium sulfate	N – $14 \times 2 = 28.00$ H – $1 \times 8 = 8.00$ S – $32 \times 1 = 32.00$ O – $16 \times 4 = \underline{64.00}$ molar mass = 132.00
$H_2O_{(l)}$	water	H – $1 \times 2 = 2.00$ O – $16 \times 1 = \underline{16.00}$ molar mass = 18.00
$NaCl_{(s)}$	sodium chloride	Na – $23.00 \times 1 = 23.00$ Cl – $35.50 \times 1 = \underline{35.50}$ molar mass = 58.50

3. 6.023×10^{23}

5. **a)** 10 g/2.02 g/mol = 4.95 mol
   b) 10 g/32.05 g/mol = 0.31 mol
   c) 10 g/129.79 g/mol = 0.08 mol

Lesson 18—WHMIS and MSDS

PRACTICE EXERCISE— ANSWERS AND SOLUTIONS

1. **a)** Compressed gas
   b) Poison
   c) Corrosive material
   d) Poison and infectious

Practice Test

PRACTICE TEST— ANSWERS AND SOLUTIONS

1.

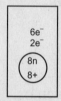 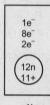 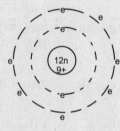

oxygen   sodium   fluorine

3.

Acid Name	Formula	Binary Acid/ Oxy Acid
nitric acid	$HNO_{3(aq)}$	Oxy acid
hydrochloric acid	$HCl_{(aq)}$	Binary acid
hydrofluoric acid	$HF_{(aq)}$	Binary acid
sulfuric acid	$H_2SO_{4(aq)}$	Oxy acid

5.

Name	Formula	Ion Charge of Metal
copper (II) nitrate	$Cu(NO_3)_2$	Cu^{2+}
Iron (III) oxide	F_2O_3	Fe^{3+}
manganese (IV) oxide	MnO_2	Mn^{4+}
Iron (II) hydroxide	$Fe(OH)_2$	Fe^{2+}

7.

Name	Atomic Symbol	Common Ion Charge
nitrogen	N	N^{3+}
lithium	Li	Li^+
sodium	Na	Na^+
oxygen	O	O^{2-}
fluorine	F	F^-
sulphur	S	S^{2-}
magnesium	Mg	Mg^{2+}

9.

Element	Atomic Number	Number of Protons	Number of Neutrons	Number of Electrons	Atomic Mass
He	2	2	2	2	4
C	6	6	6	6	12
Na	11	11	12	11	23
Cu	29	29	34	29	63

11. • Lustrous

• Malleable

• Ductile

13. a) DR $H_2SO_{4(aq)} + 2NaOH_{(aq)} \rightarrow 2H_2O_{(l)} + NaSO_{4(aq)}$

b) SR $Cu_{(s)} + 2AgNO_{3(aq)} \rightarrow Cu(NO_3)_{2(aq)} + 2Ag_{(s)}$

c) C $CH_{4(g)} + 2O_{2(g)} \rightarrow CO_{2(g)} + 2H_2O_{(l)}$

15. a) 5 moles
b) 6 moles
c) 2 moles
d) 6 moles react to give 2 moles of product

17. a) 3
b) 1
c) 4
d) 2

ENERGY FLOW IN TECHNOLOGICAL SYSTEMS

Lesson 1—Motion

PRACTICE EXERCISE— ANSWERS AND SOLUTIONS

1. **a)** $2(400 \text{ m}) + 2(550 \text{ m}) = 1\,900 \text{ m}$

b) 0, start point = finish point

3. C

$$v = \frac{d}{t}$$
$$d = (15 \text{ m/s})(5.0 \text{ s})$$
$$= 75 \text{ m}$$

5. $v = \dfrac{d}{t}$

$$= \frac{(8.0 \text{ km})(1\,000)}{(0.6 \text{ h})(60 \text{ min/h})(60 \text{ s/min})}$$
$$= 3.7 \text{ m/s}$$

7. $v = \dfrac{d}{t}$

$$t = \frac{d}{v}$$
$$= \frac{5\,000 \text{ m}}{2.5 \text{ m/s}}$$
$$= 2\,000 \text{ s}$$

9. **a)** $(1.3 \text{ m/s})(90 \text{ s}) = 117 \text{ m}$
$(0.5 \text{ m/s})(90 \text{ s}) = \underline{45 \text{ m}}$
$= 162 \text{ m}$

Direction does not matter in finding distance.

b) Average speed $= \dfrac{\text{total distance}}{\text{total time}}$

$$= \frac{162 \text{ m}}{180 \text{ s}}$$
$$= 0.9 \text{ m/s}$$

---

c) Direction does matter.

 117 m north
 − 45 m south
 = 72 m north

d) Average velocity $= \dfrac{\text{total displacement}}{\text{total time}}$

 $= \dfrac{72 \text{ m north}}{18.0 \text{ s}}$

 $= 0.4 \text{ m/s north}$

11. a) Circumference $= 2\pi r$
 $= 2(3.14)(8.50 \text{ m})$
 $= 53.4 \text{ m}$

 $\therefore v_a = \dfrac{53.4 \text{ m}}{12.0 \text{ s}}$

 $= 4.45 \text{ m/s}$

b) Since he is back to his starting point, his displacement was 0.

 $v_a = \dfrac{0 \text{ m}}{12.0 \text{ s}}$

 $= 0 \text{ m/s}$

Lesson 2—Graphical Determination Of Velocity

PRACTICE EXERCISE— ANSWERS AND SOLUTIONS

1. a)

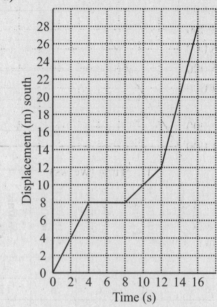

b) The slope of the graph will give velocity:

slope 0–4 s $= \dfrac{8 \text{ m}}{4 \text{ s}} = 2 \text{ m/s}$

slope 4–8 s $= \dfrac{0 \text{ m}}{4 \text{ s}} = 0 \text{ m/s}$

slope 8–12 s $= \dfrac{4 \text{ m}}{4 \text{ s}} = 1 \text{ m/s}$

slope 12–16 s $= \dfrac{16 \text{ m}}{4 \text{ s}} = 4 \text{ m/s}$

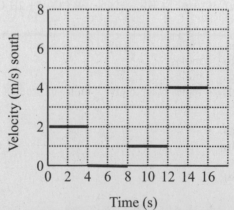

3. a)

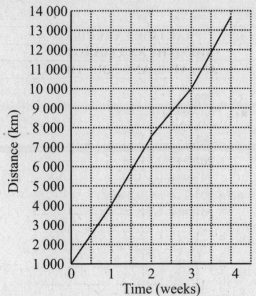

Start to Hawaii = 4 000/7 = 571.4 km/day
Hawaii to Guam = 3 500/7 = 500.0 km/day
Guam to Tokyo = 2 500/7 = 357.1 km/day
Tokyo to Hong Kong = 3 500/7 = 500 km/day

b) Guam to Tokyo

c) Start to Hawaii

d) Average speed
= (4 000 km + 3 500 km + 3 500 km
+ 2 500 km) /4 weeks
= 482.14 km/week

Lesson 3—Acceleration

PRACTICE EXERCISE— ANSWERS AND SOLUTIONS

1. $a = \dfrac{v}{t}$

$= \dfrac{10 \text{ m/s}}{2.5 \text{ s}}$

$= 4 \text{ m/s}^2$ north

3. $a = \dfrac{v_f - v_i}{t}$

$5.0 \text{ m/s}^2 = \dfrac{v_f - 20 \text{ m/s}}{3.0 \text{ s}}$

$v_f = (3.0 \text{ s})(5.0 \text{ m/s}^2) + 20 \text{ m/s}$
$= 35 \text{ m/s}$

5. $a = \dfrac{v_f - v_i}{t}$

$3.8 \text{ m/s}^2 = \dfrac{100 \text{ km/h} - 50 \text{ km/h}}{t}$

$100 \text{ km/h} = 27.8 \text{ m/s}$
$50 \text{ km/h} = 13.9 \text{ m/s}$

$t = \dfrac{27.8 \text{ m/s} - 13.9 \text{ m/s}}{3.8 \text{ m/s}^2}$

$= 3.7 \text{ s}$

7. A
$120 \text{ km/h} = 33.3 \text{ m/s}$
$50 \text{ km/h} = 13.9 \text{ m/s}$

$a = \dfrac{v_f - v_i}{t}$

$t = \dfrac{v_f - v_i}{a}$

$t = \dfrac{33.3 \text{ m/s} - 13.9 \text{ m/s}}{-11.2 \text{ m/s}}$

$= 1.73 \text{ s}$

9. $a = \dfrac{\text{rise}}{\text{run}}$

$= \dfrac{20 \text{ m/s}}{12 \text{ s}}$

$= 1.67 \text{ m/s}^2$ north

11.

$$a = \frac{v_f - v_i}{t}$$

$$30.0 \text{ m/s}^2 = \frac{1\,000 \text{ m/s} - 0}{t}$$

$$t = \frac{1\,000 \text{ m/s}}{30.0 \text{ m/s}^2}$$

$$= 33.3 \text{ s}$$

13. Since there is no change in velocity, the acceleration is zero.

Lesson 4—Acceleration Due To Gravity

PRACTICE EXERCISE—
ANSWERS AND SOLUTIONS

1. $v_f = v_i + at$
$= 0 + (9.81 \text{ m/s}^2)(3.0 \text{ s})$
$= 29.4 \text{ m/s}$

3. A

$$v_f = v_i + at$$
$$17.5 \text{ m/s} = 0 + (9.81 \text{ m/s}^2)t$$
$$t = \frac{17.5 \text{ m/s}}{9.81 \text{ m/s}^2}$$
$$= 1.78 \text{ s}$$

5.

$$t = \frac{v_f - v_i}{a}$$
$$= \frac{14 \text{ m/s} - 5.0 \text{ m/s}}{9.81 \text{ m/s}^2}$$
$$= 0.92 \text{ s}$$

7.

$$a = \frac{v_f - v_i}{t}$$
$$9.81 \text{ m/s}^2 = \frac{v_f - 0}{6.0 \text{ s}}$$
$$v_f = (9.81 \text{ m/s}^2)(6.0 \text{ s})$$
$$= 58.9 \text{ m/s}$$

Change m/s to km/h
$(58.9 \text{ m/s})(1/1\,000 \text{ km/h})(1/3\,600 \text{ s/h})$
$= 212 \text{ km/h}$

Lesson 5—Force

PRACTICE EXERCISE—
ANSWERS AND SOLUTIONS

1. $F = ma$
$= (15.0 \text{ kg})(5.5 \text{ m/s}^2)$
$= 82.5 \text{ N}$
$= 83 \text{ N}$

3.

$$F = ma$$
$$6.5 \times 10^3 \text{ N} = m(10.0 \text{ m/s}^2)$$
$$m = 6.5 \times 10^2 \text{ kg}$$

5. $a = \frac{v_f - v_i}{t}$

$$= \frac{30 \text{ m/s} - 25 \text{ m/s}}{5.2 \text{ s}}$$
$$= 0.96 \text{ m/s}^2$$
$$F = ma$$
$$= (1\,000 \text{ kg})(0.96 \text{ m/s}^2)$$
$$= 961.5 \text{ N}$$
$$= 9.6 \times 10^2 \text{ N}$$

7. a) $F = ma$

$$a = \frac{F}{m}$$
$$= \frac{20 \text{ N}}{0.026 \text{ kg}}$$
$$= 7.7 \times 10^2 \text{ m/s}^2$$

b. $a = \frac{v_f - v_i}{t}$

$$7.7 \times 10^2 \text{ m/s}^2 = \frac{v_f - 0}{0.8 \text{ s}}$$

$$v_f = 0 + (7.7 \times 10^2 \text{ m/s}^2)(0.8 \text{ s})$$
$$= 616 \text{ m/s}$$
$$= 6.2 \times 10^2 \text{ m/s}$$

9. $a = \frac{v_f - v_i}{t}$

$$= \frac{30 \text{ m/s} - 20 \text{ m/s}}{5.0 \text{ s}}$$
$$= 2 \text{ m/s}^2$$
$$F = ma$$
$$= (1\,000 \text{ kg})(2 \text{ m/s}^2)$$
$$= 2.0 \times 10^3 \text{ N}$$

Lesson 6—Work

PRACTICE EXERCISE—
ANSWERS AND SOLUTIONS

1.

J	kJ	MJ
2.00×10^3	2.00	2.00×10^{-3}
1.2×10^2	1.2×10^{-1}	1.2×10^{-4}
3.01	3.01×10^{-3}	3.01×10^{-6}

3. None, because there is no change in distance.

5. $W = Fd$

$F = \dfrac{W}{d}$

$\quad = \dfrac{1.7 \times 10^3 \text{ J}}{9.0 \text{ m}}$

$\quad = 188.9 \text{ N}$

$\quad = 1.9 \times 10^2 \text{ N}$

7. $a = \dfrac{v_f - v_i}{t}$

$\quad = \dfrac{9.8 \text{ m/s} - 0}{1.3 \text{ s}}$

$\quad = 7.54 \text{ m/s}^2$

$W = mad$

$\quad = (75 \text{ kg}) (7.54 \text{ m/s}^2) (3.2 \text{ m})$

$\quad = 1\,809.6 \text{ J}$

$\quad = 1.8 \times 10^3 \text{ J}$

9. $m = \dfrac{F}{a}$

$\quad = \dfrac{300 \text{ N}}{6.01 \text{ m/s}^2}$

$\quad = 49.9 \text{ kg}$

Lesson 7—Power

PRACTICE EXERCISE—
ANSWERS AND SOLUTIONS

1. $P = \dfrac{E}{t}$

$E = P_t$

$\quad = (100 \text{ W}) (6\,000 \text{ s})$

$\quad = 6 \times 10^5 \text{ J}$

3. B

$W = mgh$

$P = \dfrac{W}{t}$

$\quad = \dfrac{(55 \text{ kg})(9.81 \text{ m/s}^2)(2.5 \text{ m})}{3.0 \text{ s}}$

$\quad = 4.5 \times 10^2 \text{ W}$

5. $W = mgh$

$\quad = (30 \text{ kg}) (9.81 \text{ m/s}^2) (2.50 \text{ m}^2)$

$\quad = 737.75 \text{ J}$

$P = \dfrac{W}{t}$

$\quad = \dfrac{737.75 \text{ J}}{2.00 \text{ s}}$

$\quad = 3.69 \times 10^2 \text{ W}$

7. $P = \dfrac{W}{t}$

$t = \dfrac{W}{P}$

$\quad = \dfrac{300 \text{ J}}{50 \text{ W}}$

$\quad = 6.0 \text{ s}$

Lesson 8—Kinetic Energy

PRACTICE EXERCISE—
ANSWERS AND SOLUTIONS

1. $E_k = \dfrac{1}{2} mv^2$

$\quad = \dfrac{1}{2} (48 \text{ kg})(4.9 \text{ m/s})^2$

$\quad = 576.24 \text{ J}$

$\quad = 5.8 \times 10^2 \text{ J}$

3. $E_k = \frac{1}{2}mv^2$

$= \frac{1}{2}(60.0 \text{ kg})(3.50 \text{ m/s})^2$

$= 367.5 \text{ J}$

$= 368 \text{ J}$

5. $E_k = \frac{1}{2}mv^2$

$= \frac{1}{2}(50 \text{ kg})(3.5 \text{ m/s})^2$

$= 306.25 \text{ J}$

$P = \frac{E}{t}$

$= \frac{306.25 \text{ J}}{(35 \text{ min})(60 \text{ s/min})}$

$= 0.15 \text{ W}$

7. $E_k = Pt$

$P = \frac{E_k}{t}$

$= \frac{300 \text{ J}}{250 \text{ s}}$

$= 1.2 \text{ W}$

9. $E_k = \frac{1}{2}mv^2$

$5.5 \times 10^6 \text{ J} = \frac{1}{2}(1.5 \times 10^6 \text{ kg})(v)^2$

$v = \sqrt{\frac{2(5.5 \times 10^6 \text{ J})}{1.5 \times 10^6 \text{ kg}}}$

$= 2.71 \text{ m/s}$

$d = vt$

$= (2.71 \text{ m/s})(60 \text{ s})$

$= 162 \text{ m}$

$= 1.6 \times 10^2 \text{ m}$

Lesson 9—Potential Energy

PRACTICE EXERCISE— ANSWERS AND SOLUTIONS

1. **a)** potential   **b)** joules

c) $E_p = mgh$ **d)** $E_p = qV$

e) joules   **f)** kinetic

g) joules   **h)** $E_k = \frac{1}{2}mv^2$

3. $E_p = mgh$

$= (500 \text{ kg})(9.81 \text{ m/s}^2)(10 \text{ m})$

$= 4.9 \times 10^4 \text{ J}$

5. $E_p = qV$

$= (100 \text{ C})(9 \text{ V})$

$= 900 \text{ J}$

$= 9 \times 10^2 \text{ J}$

7. $W = Fd$

$= (14 \text{ N})(0.20 \text{ m})$

$= 2.8 \text{ J}$

Potential energy is the amount of work to be put into the system by Lane = 2.8 J.

9. $E_p = mgh$

$2.5 \times 10^5 \text{ J} = (m)(9.81 \text{ m/s}^2)(10 \text{ m})$

$m = \frac{2.5 \times 10^5 \text{ J}}{(9.81 \text{ m/s}^2)(10 \text{ m})}$

$= 2\,548 \text{ kg}$

$= 2.5 \times 10^3 \text{ kg}$

11. $E_p = mgh$

$5 \times 10^9 \text{ J} = m(9.81 \text{ m/s}^2)(60 \text{ m})$

$M = 8.5 \times 10^6 \text{ kg}$

Lesson 10—Mechanical Energy

PRACTICE EXERCISE—
ANSWERS AND SOLUTIONS

1. a) $E_p = mgh$
   $$= (50 \text{ kg}) (9.81 \text{ m/s}^2) (0.15 \text{ m})$$
   $$= 73.58 \text{ J}$$
   $$= 74 \text{ J}$$

   b) $E_p = E_k$
   $$73.58 \text{ J} = \frac{1}{2}(50 \text{ kg}) v^2$$
   $$v = \sqrt{\frac{2(73.58 \text{ J})}{50 \text{ kg}}}$$
   $$= 1.7 \text{ m/s downward}$$

3. A pendulum system

5. $E_p = mgh$
   $$= (1.0 \text{ kg}) (9.81 \text{ m/s}^2) (3.5 \text{ m})$$
   $$= 34.24 \text{ J}$$

   1st bounce: $34.34 - 3.434 = 30.901 \text{ J}$
   2nd bounce: $30.901 - 3.090\ 1 = 27.810\ 9 \text{ J}$
   3rd bounce: $27.810\ 9 - 2.781\ 09 = 25.0 \text{ J}$

7. A) gravitational $E_p = 500 \text{ J}$

   $\therefore$ elastic $E_p = 500 \text{ J}$

   B) $E_p = mgh$
   $$500 \text{ J} = (30 \text{ kg}) (9.81 \text{ m/s}^2) (h)$$

   $$h = \frac{500 \text{ J}}{(30 \text{ kg})(9.81 \text{ m/s}^2)}$$
   $$= 1.7 \text{ m}$$

Lesson 11—Thermodynamics

PRACTICE EXERCISE—
ANSWERS AND SOLUTIONS

1. A

3. D

5. $\dfrac{\text{Output Energy}}{\text{Input Energy}} \times 100 = \quad \%$

7. D

9. First Law: Energy is neither created nor destroyed, only converted to another form.
   Effect: Energy is transferred from the heat source to the water.

   Second Law: Heat will always flow from a higher to a lower temperature.
   Effect: Heat flows from bottom of the pot to the top — toward the cooler water.

11. a) Efficiency $= \dfrac{\text{Output Energy}}{\text{Input Energy}} \times 100$

    $$= \frac{5.5 \text{ J}}{1.5 \text{ J}} \times 100$$
    $$= \underline{367\%}$$

    b) No, unless nuclear fusion is used.

Lesson 12—Heat Engines

PRACTICE EXERCISE—
ANSWERS AND SOLUTIONS

1. The valves let in air and fuel, and let out the exhaust at the correct time.

3. A cooling system around the cylinder will keep it from expanding too much.
   The piston will expand as well so that the system remains sealed. The rings in the cylinder also expand to seal up any leaks.

5. The problem was that fuel was not being injected into the engines; these were gravity-fed. Fuel injectors were put on the engine which pushed the gas into the cylinders. This prevented stalls and power failures.

7. The engine might melt and seize up.

PRACTICE TEST

PRACTICE TEST—
ANSWERS AND SOLUTIONS

1. sunlight

3. a)

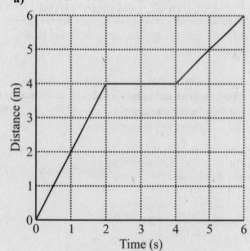

Units of time and distance will vary.

b) The object moved the fastest between 0 s and 2 s.

c) Between 0 s and 4 s, no distance was travelled, so the object must have been stopped.

5. C

7. Work

$$\text{Area} = \frac{1}{2}Fd$$

9. $\dfrac{\text{rise}}{\text{run}} = \dfrac{37 \text{ m}}{30 \text{ N}} = 1.2$

11. No, work requires a displacement.

13. Kinetic energy as well as heat energy

15. $E = Pt$
running: $(2.5 \times 10^6 \text{ J/h})\,(1.0 \text{ h}) = 2.5 \times 10^6 \text{ J}$
biking: $(3.6 \times 10^6 \text{ J/h})\,(0.75 \text{ h}) = 2.7 \times 10^6 \text{ J}$
swimming: $(5.5 \times 10^6 \text{ J/h})\,(0.5 \text{ h}) = 2.75 \times 10^6 \text{ J}$
Total $\quad = 7.95 \times 10^6 \text{ J}$
$\qquad\qquad = 8.0 \times 10^6 \text{ J}$

17. $\begin{aligned} W &= Fd \\ &= (45 \text{ N})\,(1\,500 \text{ m}) \\ &= 67\,500 \text{ J} \\ &= 6.8 \times 10^4 \text{ J} \end{aligned}$

19. $E_k = \dfrac{1}{2}mv^2$

$45 \text{ J} = \dfrac{1}{2}(m)(1.5 \text{ m/s})^2$

$m = 40 \text{ kg}$

21. Chemical

23. $\begin{aligned} E &= qV \\ 500 \text{ J} &= q(12 \text{ V}) \\ q &= 42 \text{ C} \end{aligned}$

25. $\begin{aligned} E_k &= E_p \\ \frac{1}{2}mv^2 &= mgh \\ \frac{1}{2}v^2 &= gh \end{aligned}$

$\dfrac{1}{2}(3.0 \text{ m/s})^2 = (9.81 \text{ m/s}^2)\,(h)$

$h = \dfrac{\frac{1}{2}(3.0 \text{ m/s})^2}{9.81 \text{ m/s}^2}$
$\quad = 0.46 \text{ m}$

CYCLING OF MATTER IN LIVING SYSTEMS

Lesson 1—History

PRACTICE EXERCISE—
ANSWERS AND SOLUTIONS

1. **D**

3. Responding variables are the conditions that are, measured to determine the result of changing the manipulated variable.

    Example: In an experiment to determine if the amount of sunlight affects plant growth, the manipulated variable would be the plant's growth.

5.

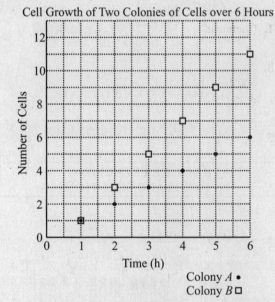

Cell Growth of Two Colonies of Cells over 6 Hours

Colony *A* •
Colony *B* □

Lesson 2   Cell Theory And Cell Types

PRACTICE EXERCISE—
ANSWERS AND SOLUTIONS

1. **D**

3. **D**

5. Answers will vary. Size, color, horns, pattern, living area

Lesson 3—Cells — Staining and Imaging

PRACTICE EXERCISE—
ANSWERS AND SOLUTIONS

1. **A**

3. Yes, as there are lenses inside the microscope as well as in the camera.

5. a) $\dfrac{1}{3} \times 0.5 \times 1\,000 = 167\,\mu m$

    b) $\dfrac{5\,mm}{0.167\,m} = 3\times$

7. a) Simple — single lens to magnify; useful for large objects

    b) Compound — two lenses; maximum magnification is 1 000 times

    c) Dark field — blocks direct light and illuminates from the side; allows a bright cell to be viewed on a black background

    d) Phase contrast — separates direct and diffracted (scattered) light from specimen; specimen can be alive

    e) Polarized — light is filtered to allow only parallel light rays through he specimen; clearer image

f) Florescent microscopes (UV light) — uses ultraviolet light on specimen, organelles glow in UVspectrum, especially useful when using florescent dyes

Lesson 4—Gene Mapping

PRACTICE EXERCISE—
ANSWERS AND SOLUTIONS

1. B

3. Isolate the DNA from the cells.
Put chemicals onto the DNA that cut it at certain places. Place the pieces into solution.
Add a charge to the solution to separate the DNA pieces. Examine the sequence of pieces and record them.

5. Answers will vary.

Lesson 5—Cell Communication

PRACTICE EXERCISE—
ANSWERS AND SOLUTIONS

1. D

3. Cytoplasm streaming moves molecules within the cell. This transports molecules to where they are needed and aids in cell movement.

Lesson 6—Cell Structure

PRACTICE EXERCISE—
ANSWERS AND SOLUTIONS

1. A

3. A

5. Amoebas stream fluid from one part of the cell to another to move. Once an amoeba has located food, chemical sensors alter membranes that change ion concentrations in one area of the cell. Fluid then flows in this direction as a result of the concentration gradient, which results in movement.

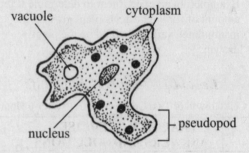

7. $C_6H_{12}O_6 + 6O_2 \rightarrow 6CO_2 + 6H_2O + ATP$

Lesson 7—Fluid Mosaic Model

PRACTICE EXERCISE—
ANSWERS AND SOLUTIONS

1.

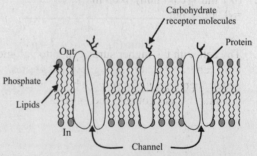

Fluid Mosaic Model of Cell Membrane

3. It can't. Water flows easily through the membrane. The lipid membrane blocks water passage, but water still seeps in.

Lesson 8—Movement Across Membranes

PRACTICE EXERCISE—
ANSWERS AND SOLUTIONS

1. **C**

3. Nerve cells pump Na^+ ions out of the cell and K^+ ions into the cell, creating a concentration gradient. The process is called active transport.

Lesson 9—Dialysis

PRACTICE EXERCISE—
ANSWERS AND SOLUTIONS

1. **A**

3. **D**

Lesson 10—Multicellular Life

PRACTICE EXERCISE—
ANSWERS AND SOLUTIONS

1. **B**

3. Volume of a sphere is $4/3\pi r^3$

$$\frac{(4)(3.14)(0.03\text{ mm})^3}{3} = 0.000\ 11\text{ mm}^3$$

5. $(0.1\text{ mm})(0.08\text{ mm})(0.05\text{ mm})$
   $= 0.000\ 4\text{ mm}^3$

7. The cell with the higher surface area to volume ratio can transfer nutrients, gases and wastes better; therefore, it can survive better when all of the nutrients are going to the muscles.

9. For cell A, if $d = 0.5$ mm, then $r = 0.25$ mm

SA of a sphere $= 4\pi r^2$

Volume or a sphere $= \dfrac{3}{4}\pi r^3$

$SA_A = (4)(3.14)(0.25\text{ mm})^2$
$= 7.9 \times 10^{-3}\text{ cm}^2$
$SA_B = (4)(3.14)(1.0\text{ cm})^2 = 12.56\text{ cm}^2$

$V_A = \left(\dfrac{3}{4}\right)(3.14)(0.25\text{ mm})^3$
$= 7.0 \times 10^{-5}\text{ cm}^3$
$V_B = \left(\dfrac{3}{4}\right)(3.14)(1.0\text{ mm})3 = 4.19\text{ cm}^3$

$SA_A/V_A = 1{:}0.89 \times 10^{-2}$
$SA_B/V_B = 1{:}0.33$ a large difference!

11. Most negative opinions about stem cells arise from the fact that stem cells from fetal material, or some believe that using stem cells interferes with the natural life cycle.

Lesson 11—Plant

PRACTICE EXERCISE—
ANSWERS AND SOLUTIONS

1. **A**

3. **D**

5. Student's diagrams must include a two to three stage process which stimuli of light and CO_2 increase the K^+ concentration of the guard cell. This draws water in by osmosis, and the cell swells. Because the outer edge of the cell is thin, the swelling expands outward, drawing the stoma open.

Lesson 12—Plant Transportation

PRACTICE EXERCISE—
ANSWERS AND SOLUTIONS

1. D

3. The movement of the bug on the leaf signals for ions to be pumped into a cell. The cell concentration gradient increases, which draws water in by osmosis. The cell swells in a direction that causes the leaf to move. A series of cells moving in sequence causes the leaves to close in on the bug.

Lesson 13—Plant Directional Growth

PRACTICE EXERCISE—
ANSWERS AND SOLUTIONS

1. A

3. The plant will move because it is light and gravity-sensitive. Turgidity and plasmosis aid the plant in moving to the best position when the plant is placed in a new location.

PRACTICE TEST

PRACTICE TEST—
ANSWERS AND SOLUTIONS

1. B

3. A. cell wall
   B. cell membrane
   C. vacuole
   D. endoplasmic reticulum
   E. ribosome
   F. nucleus
   G. golgi apparatus
   H. mitochondria
   Type of cell: plant cell

5. C

7. B

9. $\dfrac{10}{100} = \dfrac{3}{x} = 30$ mm

11. 100 000 genes, 23 pairs of chromosomes

13. Scanning Tunneling Microscope, shape, molecules

15. C

17. A

19. Exocytosis

21. The SA/V ratio would be too low to sustain life.

23. They will swell as a result of the osmotic pressure gradient

25. Carbohydrates move into the sieve and companion cells. Water is drawn in, moving the sugars along the phloem. The solution separates at the sink and water returns to the xylem.

27. A. Ocular lens
    B. Body
    C. Objective lens
    D. Stage
    E. Light
    F. Coarse adjustment
    G. Fine adjustment
    H. Arm
    I. Base

ENERGY FLOW IN GLOBAL SYSTEMS

Lesson 1—Kinetic Molecular Theory

PRACTICE EXERCISE—
ANSWERS AND SOLUTIONS

1. **D**

3. • Molecules are in motion.
   • Increasing temperature = increasing motion.
   • Increase in motion increases pressure
   • Increase in distance between atoms results in a change of state

5. Warm air plus the rotation of Earth causes air to circulate up at the equator and down at the tropics. This is known as the Coriolis Effect.

Lesson 2—Biomes

PRACTICE EXERCISE—
ANSWERS AND SOLUTIONS

1. Answers will vary. Musk Ox, and long hair travel in herds. Polar bears have white fur for camouflaged hunting.

3. **C**

5. See biome map page 227

Lesson 3—Biosphere

PRACTICE EXERCISE—
ANSWERS AND SOLUTIONS

1. **D**

3. **C**

5. **C**

7. Lithosphere

Lesson 4—Heterotrophs

PRACTICE EXERCISE—
ANSWERS AND SOLUTIONS

1. $6CO_2 + 6H_2O + Energy \rightarrow 6O_2 + C_6H_{12}O_6$

3. **B**

5. Energy is captured in small bonds of ATP and CO_2 is released along with H_2O.

Lesson 5—Systems

PRACTICE EXERCISE—
ANSWERS AND SOLUTIONS

1. Answers will vary; there may be transfer of energy to other systems, but no transfer of matter.

3. No, all living things must interact at some point. Only dormant viruses can exist in an isolated environment.

5. Give an example that involves only the exchange of energy between systems;
   eg. Earth in the solar system.

Lesson 6—Specific Heat Of Water

PRACTICE EXERCISE—
ANSWERS AND SOLUTIONS

1. Q $= mc\Delta t$
   $= (1\,000 \text{ g}) (4.19 \text{ J/g°C}) (98°C - 15°C)$
   $= 3.48 \times 10^5 \text{ J}$

3. 3 kg $= 3\,000 \text{ g}$

   $Q = mc\Delta t$
   $15\,000 \text{ J} = (3\,000 \text{ g}) (4.19 \text{ J/g°C}) (\Delta t)$

   $\Delta t = \dfrac{15\,000 \text{ J}}{(3\,000 \text{ g})(4.19 \text{ J/g°C})}$

   $= 1.20°C$

5.
$$Q = mc\Delta t$$
$$230\ 000\ \text{J} = (4\ 000\ \text{g})\ (4.19\ \text{J/g°C})\ (\Delta t)$$

$$\Delta t = \frac{(4\ 000\ \text{g})(4.19\ \text{J/g°C})}{230\ 000\ \text{J}}$$
$$= 0.073\text{°C}$$

7. $Q = mc\Delta t$
$= (4200\ \text{g})\ (4.16\ \text{J/g°C})\ (50.0\text{°C})$
$= 8.74 \times 10^5\ \text{J}$

Lesson 7—Water

PRACTICE EXERCISE—
ANSWERS AND SOLUTIONS

1. $Q = mH_f$
$= (100\ \text{g})\ (333\ \text{J/g})$
$= 33\ 300\ \text{J}$
$= 3.33 \times 10^4\ \text{J}$

3. $Q = mH_v$
$= (100\ \text{g})\ (2\ 260\ \text{J/g})$
$= 2.26 \times 10^5\ \text{J}$

5. $90\text{°C} - 1\text{°C} = 89\text{°C}$

$Q = mc\Delta t$
$= (1\ 000\ \text{g})\ (4.19\ \text{J/g°C})\ (89\text{°C})$
$= 3.73 \times 10^5\ \text{J}$

7. $Q = mH_v$
$= (20\ 000\ \text{g})\ (2\ 260\ \text{J/g})$
$= 4.52 \times 10^7\ \text{J}$

Lesson 8—Water And Weather

PRACTICE EXERCISE—
ANSWERS AND SOLUTIONS

1. Heat is released when water vapour condenses into liquid water. The excess heat causes the moist air to rise and draws up more moist air, causing the cycle to repeat itself.
Air cannot hold heat because its heat capacity is small compared with that of water.

3. Hot air is less dense than cool air and therefore rises. Cool air, being more dense, falls.

5. Fast rising air rains and speeds up drawing more moist air up. Large releases of energy build up static electricity.

Lesson 9—Air Pressures

PRACTICE EXERCISE—
ANSWERS AND SOLUTIONS

1. Earth's rotation bends the prevailing winds. They trail off toward the west.

3. B

5. Because of Earth's rotation, the wind is circulated from the northwest and high pressure areas develop at the 60° latitude. The mountains to the west of us cause the winds to be channeled down from the arctic.

Lesson 10—Weather Systems

PRACTICE EXERCISE—
ANSWERS AND SOLUTIONS

1. B

3. Westerlies rise and shed their water over the Coastal Mountains and Rockies and then release heat as they fall down the eastern slopes of the Rockies.

5. Labrador current, Gulf Stream, and Alaskan current.

Lesson 11—Relative Humidity

PRACTICE EXERCISE—
ANSWERS AND SOLUTIONS

1. a) 40%
b) 9%
c) 55%

3. 17.7°C

5. D

7. Kinetic Molecular Theory of Matter – there is more space between atoms in hot air than in cold air.

Lesson 12—Weather Prediction

PRACTICE EXERCISE—
ANSWERS AND SOLUTIONS

1. False

3. • Geostationary
   • Polar satellite

5. • Radar
   • Satellites
   • Maps

7. Northern Quebec

9. Fog would develop in the Gulf of St. Lawrence as a result of the meeting of a warm air front and cool air from the north.

11. Answers will vary.

Lesson 13—Climate Graphs

PRACTICE EXERCISE—
ANSWERS AND SOLUTIONS

1. A

3. All temperatures and rainfall increase in July or August.

5. The summer months

PRACTICE TEST

PRACTICE TEST—
ANSWERS AND SOLUTIONS

1. Rotation causes winds of different speeds at different latitudes. These winds are bent (the Coriolis Effect).

3. C

5. True.
   Decomposers, such as fungus, break down decaying tissue and release molecules into the ground and atmosphere.

7. B

9. • Stop using CFCs
   • Properly dispose of CFCs from refrigerators, freezers, air conditioners, etc.
   • Become educated on how to build up ozone

11. Water holds heat well, thereby preventing rapid changes in weather.

13. B

15. $Q = mc\Delta t$
    $= (20\ 000\ \text{g})\ (4.19\ \text{J/g°C})\ (10°\text{C})$
    $= 8.4 \times 10^5\ \text{J}$

17. joules/grams

19. • Warm moist air rises over coast mountains
    • Precipitation – releases energy
    • Repeated over Rocky Mountains
    • Air drops onto prairies
    • Heat created by high pressure

21. A cycling wind from a high to a low pressure area

23. The difference is large. The air is not carrying a lot of water.

25. Dew

27. Wet

29.
    condensation ←
    ↓   evaporation
    precipitation →

NOTES

APPENDICES

APPENDIX A

Significant Digits

Digits that are the result of careful measurement are called significant digits. Significant digits indicate the accuracy of the measurement.
The greater the number of significant digits, the greater the accuracy of the measurement.

1. All non-zero digits are always significant.

2. Zeros between two non-zero numbers are always significant. For example, 1.01 has three significant digits.

3. Zeros at the end of a number and after the decimal point are significant. For example, 2.20 has three significant digits.

4. Unless otherwise specified, all trailing zeros in a whole number must be considered not significant. For example, 300 has only one significant digit.

5. Zeros at the beginning of a number are never significant. For example, 0.004 5 has two significant digits.

6. When adding or subtracting measurements, the answer cannot be more precise than the least precise measurement. Therefore, the answer is expressed with the same number of decimal places as the least precise measurement. For example, 8.98 + 15.682 = 24.662 = 24.7

7. When multiplying or dividing measurements, the answer cannot be more certain than the least certain value used. Therefore, the answer is expressed with the same number of significant digits as the least certain value. For example, 59.097/3.45 = 17.129 57 = 17.13

Scientific Notation

To work with extremely large or small numbers, scientists express numbers in a simpler form called scientific notation. In scientific notation, the correct number of significant digits (with one whole number to the left of the decimal point) is multiplied by a power of 10 raised to a positive or negative exponent. To convert a number to scientific notation:

1. Move the decimal point so that only one whole number is to the left of it.

2. Delete any non-significant zeros.

3. Multiply by 10^n where n is the number of places that the decimal point has been moved.
   If the decimal point was moved to the right, then n is negative. If the decimal point was moved to the left, then n is positive. For example, the speed of light, 300 000 000 m/s, expressed in scientific notation is $3 \times 10^8 \, \text{m/s}$.

APPENDIX B

Useful Equations

Physics
$$v = \frac{\Delta d}{\Delta t} \qquad a = \frac{\Delta d}{\Delta t}$$

$$F = ma \qquad W = Fd$$

$$E_p = mgh \qquad E_k = \frac{1}{2}mv^2$$

$$\% \text{ efficiency} = \frac{\text{useful energy output}}{\text{total energy input}} \times 100\%$$

Weather
$$Q = mc\Delta T \qquad Q = \Delta H_{fus} m$$

$$Q = \Delta T_{vap} m \qquad m = DV$$

APPENDIX C

Table 1 System of Prefixes

Prefix	Symbol	Multiplication factor
exa–	E	$100\,000\,000\,000\,000\,000 = 10^{18}$
peta–	P	$100\,000\,000\,000\,000 = 10^{15}$
tera–	T	$100\,000\,000\,000 = 10^{12}$
giga–	G	$100\,000\,000 = 10^{9}$
mega–	M	$1\,000\,000 = 10^{6}$
kilo–	k	$1000 = 10^{3}$
hecto–	h	$100 = 10^{2}$
deca–	da	$10 = 10^{1}$
deci–	d	$0.1 = 10^{-1}$
centi–	c	$0.01 = 10^{-2}$
milli–	m	$0.001 = 10^{-3}$
micro–	μ	$0.000\,001 = 10^{-6}$
nano–	n	$0.000\,000\,001 = 10^{-9}$
pico–	p	$0.000\,000\,000\,001 = 10^{-12}$
femto–	f	$0.000\,000\,000\,000\,001 = 10^{-15}$
atto–	a	$0.000\,000\,000\,000\,000\,001 = 10^{-18}$

Table 2 SI Base Units

Quantity	Unit	Symbol
length/ distance	metre	m
mass	kilogram	kg
time	second	s
electric current	ampere	A
temperature	degree Celsius	°C
amount of substance	mole	mol

Table 3 Derived Units

Quantity	Unit	Symbol	Expressed in other units
force	newton	N	$kg \times m/s^2$
pressure	pascal	Pa	N/m^2
air pressure	kilopascal	kPa	$1000\,N/m^2$
energy/ work/ heat	joule / calorie	J / cal	$N \times m$, kgm^2/s^2
power	watt	W	J/s
electric charge	coulomb	C	$A \times s$
Electric potential and electromotive force	volt	V	W/A
electrical energy	kilowatt hour	kWh	
area	square metre	m^2	
volume	metre cubed	m^3	
linear speed	metre per second	m/s	
acceleration (linear)	metre per second squared	m/s^2	
frequency	hertz	Hz	
density	kilogram per cubic metre	kg/m^3	
specific heat capacity	joule per kilogram by degree celsius	$\dfrac{J}{g°C}$	
heat of fusion/heat of vaporization/ heat of combustion	joule per kilogram joule per mole	J/kg J/mol	
molar mass	gram per mole	g/mol	

acceleration: a change in velocity (speed) over time; an increase (positive acceleration) or decrease (negative acceleration) in velocity over time; expressed in units of m/s^2

acid: a solution that contains hydrogen atoms and has a pH of less than 7; aqueous solution that contains hydrogen ions $\left(H^+\right)$ and has a pH of less than 7

active transport: movement of molecules requiring the use of energy (usually in the form of ATP) and membrane proteins; used for movement of molecules against their concentration gradient

adenosine diphosphate: a molecule that functions in the transfer of energy in living cells; formed by loss of one phosphate group from ATP; composed of one molecule of adenosine, one molecule of ribose, and two phosphate groups

adenosine triphosphate (ATP): a molecule that is the primary source of energy in all living cells; the energy is stored in high-energy chemical bonds between the phosphate groups; composed of one adenosine molecule, one ribose molecule, and three phosphate groups

adhesion: a molecular force of attraction between unlike substances

aerobic respiration: see *cellular respiration*; respiration in which oxygen is a reactant

ADP: see *adenosine diphosphate*

air mass: a relatively large volume of atmospheric gas that possesses fairly uniform temperature and humidity

air pressure: the force exerted by air per unit area expressed in units of N/m^2

alkali metal: a metallic element that is a member of Group 1 of the Periodic Table

alkaline: see *base*

altitude: in *weather*, height above sea level

altocumulus cloud: *alto* is a prefix for high altitude, and a cumulus cloud is large and piled; e.g., in the form of a thundercloud

anaerobic respiration: see *cellular respiration*; respiration in which oxygen is not used as a reactant

antibiotic: a chemical or protein that causes bacterial cells to die or stop reproducing

atmosphere: the thin, gaseous layer that surrounds and protects Earth (or other heavenly body). Earth's atmosphere is comprised (in order of decreasing concentration) of nitrogen, oxygen, carbon dioxide, water vapour, and other rare gases; one portion of the biosphere

atom: the smallest unit of an element that retains the properties of that element; comprised of a nucleus (containing positively charged protons plus neutrons possessing neutral charge) orbited by negatively charged electrons

atomic mass (M): the mass of an isotope of an element measured in atomic mass units; or, the average mass of one mole $\left(6.02\times10^{23}\right)$ of atoms of an element

atomic mass unit (amu): a unit of mass equal to 1/12 of the mass of the carbon-12 atom; used to express the mass of one neutron or proton; approximately $1.67\times10^{-27}\,kg$

atomic number: the number of protons within the nucleus of one atom of an element; the elements are arranged in order of increasing atomic number in the Periodic Table of the elements

ATP: see *adenosine triphosphate*

autotroph: an organism that is capable of producing food from simple inorganic materials and energy captured by photosynthesis (or chemosynthesis); e.g. plants

average speed $\left(v_{ave}\right)$**:** the total displacement of an object divided by the time interval over which the displacement occurred; measured in units of m/s

base: aqueous solution contains hydroxide ions $\left(OH^-\right)$ and has a pH of greater than 7

binary fission: the process of cell division used by prokaryotes; e.g. bacteria, to generate multiple identical cells from one parent cell

binary ionic compounds: an ionic compound containing only two elements, one metal and one non-metal

binary molecular compound: a compound containing two non-metallic elements that are joined by a covalent bond

biosphere: an approximately 15 km thick region within and above Earth's crust that supports all life on Earth; composed of the atmosphere, hydrosphere, and lithosphere

boiling point: the temperature at which a substance evaporates (undergoes a phase change form a liquid to a gas)

carbohydrate: also *sugar*, e.g. glucose; a molecule composed of carbon, hydrogen, and oxygen atoms in the form of $C_nH_{2n}O_n$

cathode ray tube: a vacuum tube in which a stream of electrons are emitted from a piece of metal and accelerated toward a screen

cell cycle: in eukaryotic cells, the cycle of events between formation of one cell and its division into two daughter cells; composed of the phases of interphase (including G1, S, and G2) and mitosis (including prophase, metaphase, anaphase, and telophase)

cell membrane: also *plasma membrane*, the semipermeable layer of tissue that surrounds the plasma (cytoplasm)

cellular metabolism: the total of all cellular processes and chemical reactions involved in the inter-conversion of matter and energy

cellular respiration: also *aerobic respiration*, the process by which living organisms release the energy in organic compounds using oxygen (or another reactant) in the mitochondria

cell wall: a membrane that surrounds the outer surface of the cell membrane in plants and some prokaryotes for the purpose of protection and support

charge: a specific amount of electricity that a particle contains, usually due to a lack or excess of electrons

chemical bond: a force that joins two or more atoms in a molecule; chemical bonds are classified as ionic (a bond between a non-metal and a metal) or molecular (a bond between two non-metals)

chemical change: a reaction in which new substances having different chemical structures, and different properties, are formed

chemical equation: an expression representing a chemical reaction in which the formula(s) of the reactant(s) appear on the left and the formula(s) of the product(s) appear on the right; usually includes the balanced molar quantities of each reactant and product; see also *reaction equation*

chemical formula: a set of chemical symbols that identify a chemical compound; e.g., the chemical formula for glucose is

chemical potential energy: the energy that is stored in the chemical bonds of an atom; expressed in units of joules (J)

chemical property: a description of how a substance reacts chemically with another substance; any characteristic of a compound or an element that is due to its chemical structure or composition

chemical reaction: see *reaction*

chemical waste: the unused or unwanted products of a chemical reaction

chemosynthesis: the process used by some organisms (bacteria) to capture energy from inorganic molecules such as hydrogen sulphide, hydrogen, sulfur, and ammonia

chlorophyll: a pigment that absorbs light and is involved in the conversion of light energy into chemical energy; in eukaryotes, chlorophyll is stored in chloroplasts

chloroplast: an organelle in a eukaryotic photosynthetic cell that contains the chlorophyll pigment, and that functions in the conversion of light energy into chemical energy

chromosome: a strand of DNA in which genetic information of an organism is contained; chromosomes are found in the nucleus of a eukaryotic cell during interphase of the cell cycle and in the cytoplasm during mitosis

cirrus cloud: *cirrus* means "curl of hair"; the cloud is shaped like a thin wisp or curl

climate: a description of the general trends in weather occurring in a given location over a long time period

closed circulatory system: of an organism, the circulatory fluid is contained and circulated throughout the body within enclosed vessels

closed system: a system that does not exchange matter, but does exchange energy with its surroundings

coefficients (in a reaction equation): the numbers that indicate the relative amounts of each species that take part in a chemical reaction; can be read in terms of molecules or moles

cohesion: a molecular force of attraction between like substances

combustion reaction: also *oxidation reaction*, an exothermic chemical reaction in which oxygen is a reactant

compound: a pure substance with constant chemical composition and properties that is composed of two or more joined elements inseparable by ordinary physical methods

concentration gradient: the difference in concentration of a molecule/substance between two points in space

condense: to change the state of a substance from a gas into a liquid; a physical change

conductor: a material through which charged particles or heat flow freely; any substance that conducts heat or light

consumer: a heterotroph that feeds on producers and/or consumers of a lower trophic level

controlled variable: a condition that is kept constant throughout an experiment; any experimental result, therefore, cannot be attributed to the controlled variable

convection current: transfer of heat between warm and cool liquids or gases that occurs as a result of their difference in density

convection: thermal energy (heat) transfer by circulation in liquids and gases

Coriolis Effect: the deflection of Earth's moving air currents caused by Earth's rotation

corrosion: the process in which a substance is worn away gradually through a chemical reaction

covalent bond: a chemical bond formed between two atoms that share electrons

covalent compound: see *molecular compound*

cumulus cloud: cumulus means "pile"; a cloud that is thick and piled horizontally; e.g. the shape of a thundercloud

cytoplasm: region of a cell that is enclosed by the plasma membrane and that includes all cellular organelles except the nucleus

decay: to deteriorate or decompose through a biological or nuclear change

deceleration: a decrease in velocity (speed) over time; expressed in units of $\frac{m}{s^2}$

decomposers: heterotrophs that obtain their energy from non-living plant and animal (organic) remains

decomposition reaction: a chemical change in which a compound is separated into component

density: in *physics*, mass per unit volume expressed in units of g/L; the number of molecules of a substance that occupy a particular volume

deoxyribonucleic acid: abbreviated *DNA*, the chemical that composes genetic material

dependent variable: see *responding variable*

development, biological: the process of cell division, differentiation, and growth of an organism

dialysis: the separation of solutes by a semipermeable membrane; e.g., solutes can be removed from one solution and transmitted into another by diffusion through a semipermeable membrane across which a concentration gradient exists for that particular solute; e.g., in kidney dialysis to remove urine from the blood

differentiation: the process by which cells become specialized in structure, function, and division of labour during development

diffusion: the passive dispersal of molecules; direction of net movement of molecules of one type is from an area of high concentration to an area of low concentration of the molecule in question, and disregarding the concentration of molecules of other types in the same areas

digestive system: animal system by which ingested food is stored and processed by chemical and mechanical means to provide the body with absorbable nutrients and by which waste materials are excreted

dissolve: when a solid is mixed into a solution and it becomes part of the solution

DNA: see *deoxyribonucleic acid*

double replacement reaction: a chemical reaction in which two ions exchange places between two reactants

ecosystem: a self-regulating system involving the flow of energy and matter between a community of living organisms and their environment

efficiency: the ratio of useful energy (work accomplished) to the total energy input (energy supplied) during an energy conversion process; often expressed as a percentage

elastic energy: the energy stored in an object that is deformed (stretched, twisted, or compressed) and able to return to its original shape once the forces causing deformation are removed; expressed in units of joules (J)

electrical energy: the energy of electrical charges; *electrical potential energy* is derived from the force between charged particles (a force of attraction exists between two particles of unlike charge, and a force of repulsion exists between particles of like charge).

electromagnetic radiation: energy of an electromagnetic wave

electromagnetic wave: a wave consisting of oscillating (smooth changes in direction back and forth) electric and magnetic fields that travels at the speed of light

electron: a stable, sub-atomic particle that has a negative charge and a mass of 9.11×10^{-31} kg

electron cloud: the region in an atom in which there is a probability of an electron being located; this region surrounds the nucleus in the Electron Cloud Model of the atom proposed by Louis de Broglie and Erwin Schrodinger in 1930

element: a pure substance that is composed of only one kind of atom and that cannot undergo a decomposition reaction into a simpler substance

endocytosis: method of intake of materials from the environment by a living cell whereby the cell membrane progressively folds inward and around material on the outside surface of the cell until the cell membrane completely wraps around the material taken up; the membrane-enclosed material is a food vacuole when it is completely inside the cell

endoplasmic reticulum: an organelle in a eukaryotic cell; a network of tubes that function in transport of materials and provide a site for some chemical reactions in a cell; rough endoplasmic reticulum possesses associated ribosomes, which the smooth endoplasmic reticulum lacks

endothermic reaction: any change that absorbs energy (usually in the form of heat) from its surroundings, resulting in a net chemical potential energy gain in the system

energy: the ability of an object or system to perform work; expressed in units of joules (J)

environment: the surrounding space in a system, including the atmosphere, land, water, and influence of other organisms; or the space surrounding a cell

enzymes: proteins whose function is to catalyze (speed up) chemical reactions that occur in organisms

eukaryotes: cells (eukaryotic) that possess a membrane-bound ("true") nucleus and membrane-bound organelles; also, multicellular organisms that are made up of eukaryotic cells

eukaryotic cells: cells that possess a true nucleus and membrane-bound organelles

evaporate: to change the state of a substance from a liquid into a gas; a physical change

excretion: the elimination of metabolic waste from blood and tissue of an organism: e.g., in the form of urine in animals

excretory system: the system in animals that is responsible for excretion; see *excretion*

exocytosis: method of removal of wastes from a living cell whereby the membrane of a vacuole containing waste material fuses with the cell membrane such that the contents of the vacuole are exposed to and then diffuse into the external environment

exothermic reaction: any change that releases energy (usually in the form of heat) into its surroundings, resulting in a net chemical potential energy loss in the system

facilitated diffusion: also facilitated passive transport, the passive movement of molecules across a semipermeable membrane down the concentration gradient but aided by a protein/channel embedded in the membrane

family: see *group*

feedback system: a self-regulated system in which inputs to the system affect the outputs and vice versa, for the purpose of maintaining a steady state

First Law of Thermodynamics: states that matter cannot be created or destroyed; note that matter can be converted into energy without breaking the First Law; also known as the Law of Conservation of Mass or the Law of Conservation of Energy

food web: the network of feeding patterns within an ecosystem and in which most or all organisms have more than one food source; distinguished from a food chain in which each organism feeds only on the single organism present in the trophic level below its own

food: any substance (liquid or solid) that is ingested by a living organism to provide nutrients for life

force: an influence that causes an object to accelerate with a magnitude proportional to the object's mass; expressed in units of newtons (N)

formation reaction: a chemical reaction in which simple elements combine to form larger, more complex compounds; also known as a *synthesis reaction*

freeze: to change the state of a substance from a liquid into a solid; a physical change

freezing point: the temperature at which a substance undergoes a phase change from a liquid to a solid

friction: the force opposing the motion of two surfaces that are in contact

front: the zone of transition between two air masses that differ; e.g., in temperature, humidity

fundamental particle: see *sub-atomic particle*

generator: a machine that converts one form of energy to another, especially mechanical to electrical into electrical energy

glycogen: a carbohydrate that is used for storage of chemical energy in animals

Golgi apparatus or Golgi complex: an organelle in a eukaryotic cell; a network of flattened sacs that function in modification, packaging, and transport of proteins

gradient: a difference in concentration between two areas

gravitational potential energy: the stored energy of an object due to its position relative to a gravitational force; expressed in units of joules (J)

gravity: the force of attraction exerted by a body of mass, e.g., Earth on another body of mass, e.g., any object falling to Earth

group: also *family*, on the Periodic Table of the Elements, contains all the elements within a vertical column; elements of a group share similar chemical properties

halogen: a non-metallic element that is a member of Group 17 on the Periodic Table

heat: a form of energy that causes a change in the vibration of a substance's molecules, and can be transferred from one substance to another; also known as *thermal energy*

heat budget: the total amount of energy received and lost by Earth

heat capacity: a measure of the amount of energy that is required to change the temperature of a substance by one degree celsius (°C)

heat of combustion $\left(\delta H_c\right)$: the measure of the amount of heat that is released by an exothermic combustion reaction

heat of fusion $\left(\delta H_{fus}\right)$: the amount of energy that is released by one kilogram of a substance as it undergoes the physical change from a liquid to a solid

heat of vaporization $\left(\delta H_{vap}\right)$: a measure of the amount of energy that is required to change one kilogram of a substance from a liquid into a vapour

heat: thermal energy being transferred from one area to another

hemoglobin: a molecule in red blood cells that binds and carries oxygen for the purpose of transporting oxygen from the lungs to the tissues of the body

hemolymph: in organisms with open circulatory systems, the fluid that bathes tissues and transports gases and nutrients throughout the body

heterotroph: an organism that obtains its nutrients by consuming autotrophs and/ or other heterotrophs (consumers), or by consuming organic remains of dead plants and animals (decomposers)

homeostasis: steady-state of all biological functions maintained in an organism

hormone: a protein that functions to transmit signals within a multicellular body; e.g. growth hormone in humans signals growth, cell division

humidity: the concentration of water vapour in the air

hydrogen bond: a strong non-covalent bond that forms (between polar molecules) between a hydrogen atom possessing a slight positive charge within a molecule and an atom possessing a slight negative charge in the same or a different molecule; e.g. water molecules are held together by hydrogen bonds between the hydrogen atoms and the oxygen atoms that are slightly negatively charged

hydrogen halide: a compound of hydrogen with one of the halogen (Group 17) elements

hydrologic cycle: the continuous cycling of water between the atmosphere and the surface of Earth when water evaporates and condenses using solar energy (energy of the sun)

hydrosphere: the portion of Earth's biosphere that is comprised of all of the water on Earth

hypertonic solution: a solution that has a higher concentration of solutes, e.g., salts, as compared with another solution; or, a solution that has a lower concentration of solvent, e.g., water, as compared with another solution

hypotonic solution: a solution that has a lower concentration of solutes, e.g. salts, as compared with another solution; or, a solution that has a higher concentration of solvent, e.g. water, as compared with another solution

independent variable: see *manipulated variable*

inefficiency: the fraction of energy lost in an energy conversion process

inertia: the tendency of an object to resist change in motion

inorganic compound: a chemical compound that occurs naturally but is not usually *produced* by living organisms; e.g., oxygen, carbon dioxide, water, and minerals are inorganic compounds; an inorganic compound usually does not include covalent bonds between carbon atoms

insoluble: incapable of being dissolved

instantaneous speed: the speed/velocity of an object at a defined moment

ion: an atom that has an excess or lack of electrons and is therefore either positively or negatively charged

ionic bond: the attraction between two or more ions that have opposite charges (a metallic ion and a non-metallic ion)

ionic compound: a compound made up of metallic and non-metallic ions that share ionic bonds

ionic size: the size of a charged atom

ionized atom: an atom that has an excess or lack of electrons and is therefore either positively or negatively charged; an ion

isobar: curved lines on a weather map that connect areas having the same pressure after allowing for differences in height above sea level

isolated system: a system that does not exchange matter or energy with its surroundings

isothermic: having the same temperature
isotonic solution: solutions having the same concentration of a particular molecule

isotopes: elements that have the same atomic number but a different mass number; that is, elements that contain the same number of protons but a different amount of neutrons

kinetic energy: energy possessed by an object due to its motion; expressed in units of joules (J)

Kinetic Molecular Theory: the theory that states that all matter is made up of particles that are in constant random motion and that thermal energy (heat) is produced by the speed of this random motion

latitude: the distance of a point on Earth's surface measured from the equator in either a north or south direction; expressed as an angular distance in degrees

Law of Conservation of Energy: a law stating that energy can not be created or destroyed, but it can be converted to another form; also known as the *First Law of Thermodynamics*

Law of Conservation of Mass: a law stating that matter can not be created or destroyed; see also *First Law of Thermodynamics*

lenticel: opening in the stem of a plant through which gas exchange occurs and through which water escapes by transpiration

liquid: a state of matter that identifies the substance as being a fluid and being able to be poured

lithosphere: the portion of Earth's biosphere comprised of all land on Earth, including all land formations

longitude: the distance of a point on Earth's surface measured from the meridian to the Prime meridian (in Greenwich, England); expressed as an angular distance in degrees

lysosome: a cellular organelle that functions in degradation and removal of cellular waste in eukaryotes; contains hydrolytic enzymes that digest cell waste; has an acidic internal environment

manipulated variable: also *independent variable*, the variable in an experiment that is altered between trials; an experiment tests the effect of changing this variable on the experimental outcome

mass: a measure of the quantity of matter that an object contains; mass is one property that all matter possesses

---

mass number (A): the number of protons plus neutrons in the nucleus of an atom

matter: anything that possesses mass and occupies space

mechanical energy: the sum of potential and kinetic energy expressed in units of joules (J)

mechanical mixture: a mixture in which the individual components remain unaltered and visible

meiosis: the process used by eukaryotic cells for sexual reproduction; the process by which one parent cell divides to produce four cells, each having one-half the genetic material of the parent cell

melt: to change the state of a substance from a solid into a liquid; a physical change

melting point: the temperature at which a substance will undergo a physical change from a solid to a liquid; the melting point of a substance is a physical property of that substance

metabolic rate: the rate of energy conversion and use in a living organism

metabolism: all the chemical processes occurring in a living organism and that are responsible for the conversion and use of energy

metal: elements possessing some or all of the following properties: strong, hard, durable, ductile, malleable, reflects light when polished, conducts heat, conducts electricity; usually forms ions that have a positive charge; metals are found on the left side of the Periodic Table

metalloid: an element that has some properties of a metal and some properties of a non-metal; examples of metalloids are silicon and bismuth

mitochondrion: plural *mitochondria*, an organelle in a eukaryotic cell that functions in the conversion of chemical energy (e.g., glucose) into useable energy (in the form of ATP); also known as the "powerhouse" of the cell

mitosis: the part of the eukaryotic cell cycle during which one cell divides into two and during which the genetic material is precisely divided

mixture: a substance made up of one or more pure components that are not chemically bonded to one another, can be separated by physical means, and whose properties depend on the identity and ratio of the components; one of the two major classifications of matter (the other classification being a *pure substance)*

model: a representation of a system showing how the parts of a system are related; or, a theory or diagram that attempts to simplify a complex idea or system; e.g., the Electron Cloud Model of the atom

molar mass: the measure of the mass of one mole $\left(6.02\times10^{23}\right)$ of molecules of an element of compound, measured in grams per mole (g/mol)

molar ratio: the ratio of moles (coefficients) of individual reactants and products in a balanced chemical equation

mole (mol): the amount of a substance that contains 6.02×10^{23} (Avogadro's Number) particles; also, the amount of a substance (expressed in grams (g)) that corresponds to the molecular weight of the substance, usually the mass of on molecule of the substance

molecular compound: a compound that is formed from two or more non-metallic ions that share covalent bonds; molecular compounds usually have a low melting point and are non-conductors; also known as *covalent compounds*

molecular elements: elements that consist of two or more atoms of the same type; e.g., oxygen gas, which is made up of two oxygen atoms $\left(O_2\right)$

molecular formula: see *chemical formula*

molecule: the smallest particle into which an element or compound can be divided while still retaining its chemical and physical properties

momentum: a vector quantity describing the motion of an object as its mass multiplied by its velocity; expressed in units of $kg\times m/s$

motile organism: an organism that is capable of movement independent of other moving bodies

motion: the change in position of an object

multi-thermic: having many different temperatures

mutation: in genetic material, a mistake in the DNA code that contains information or instructions for the building of proteins and, thereby, the normal function of the cell

net charge: the total charge of a particle or an object after all of the positive and negative charges within it have been added together

neutral: *chemistry*-a substance that is not acidic or basic and has a pH of 7.0; *physics*-a particle or object that has a net electrical charge of zero

neutralization reaction: a reaction involving an acid and a base in which the products have a pH of 7.0

neutron: a neutrally charged subatomic particle that is contained within the nucleus and has a mass of approximately 1.68×10^{-27} kg

noble gas: an element with low reactivity that belongs to Group 18 on the Periodic Table

non-ionized atom: an atom that does not have an excess or lack of electrons and is, therefore, neutral in charge

non-metal: an element that lacks the characteristics of a metal, and is found on the right side of the Periodic Table; they occur naturally in solid, liquid, and gaseous states

non-reactive: a chemical that does not take part in chemical reactions

non-uniform motion: motion that is not at a constant speed

nuclear energy: the potential energy that is stored within the nucleus of an atom and that is released during nuclear reactions such as fission and fusion

nuclear envelope: the semipermeable membrane that encloses the nucleus within a eukaryotic cell; also, *nuclear membrane*

nuclear membrane: see *nuclear envelope* **nuclear energy** the potential energy that is contained within the nucleus of an atom and that is released during nuclear reactions such as fission and fusion

nuclear fission: a highly exothermic nuclear reaction in which the nucleus of an atom splits into two or more smaller fragments

nuclear fusion: a highly exothermic nuclear reaction in which two nuclei are combined to form a larger nucleus

nuclear reaction: a process that causes a change in the nucleus of an atom; see also nuclear fission and nuclear fusion

nucleus: *biology*-organelle in a eukarytoic cell that contains genetic information and controls the operations of the cell; *chemistry* and *physics*-a dense area in the center of an atom that contains neutrons and protons

open circulatory system: a circulatory system in which the fluid (hemolymph) is pumped by a heart to different areas of the body in vessels and then escapes from vessels to the surrounding tissue, bathing cells directly to facilitate exchange of nutrients and waste

open system: a system that exchanges both matter and energy with its surroundings

organelle: a part of a eukaryotic cell that is enclosed by a semipermeable membrane and possesses a specialized structure and function

organic compound: a substance that is found in, or produced by, a living system and that contains carbon atoms bonded covalently

osmoregulation: the control of water (therefore, ion-a solute) balance in an organism

osmosis: the diffusion of water from an area of higher concentration to an area of lower concentration of water

oxidation reaction: see *combustion reaction*

oxide: a compound made up of the atoms of oxygen and another element parts that are simpler than the original compound

passive transport: diffusion of substances across a semipermeable membrane; occurs without the use of energy

periods: horizontal rows on the Periodic Table that consist of elements with increasing atomic numbers

pH: a measure of the concentration of hydrogen ions $\left(H^+\right)$ in a solution; a measure of the acidity or alkalinity of a substance

phase: see *state*

phase change: a physical change in which a substance is transformed from one state to another; e.g. the change of water into ice is a phase change from a solid into a liquid

phloem: in a plant, vascular tissue composed of living cells that functions in the transport of food (nutrients)

photosynthesis: the process by which carbon dioxide and water are chemically converted to oxygen and glucose using solar energy; occurs in green plants and other organisms containing pigments (e.g. chlorophyll) that function in capturing light energy

physical change: a change that does not result in either the formation of a new substance(s), or a change in chemical composition

physical property: a property of a substance that describes the conditions under which a substance can undergo a physical change; e.g., the melting point of a substance

plasma membrane: see *cell membrane*

polar molecule: a molecule in which one end possesses a slight charge (either negative or positive) and the opposite end of the molecule possesses a slight opposite charge; e.g. water molecule

potential energy: stored energy as a result of position or condition of an object; expressed in units of joules (J)

power: rate of energy consumption; expressed in units of watts (W)

precipitate: a solid that is separated from a solution during a chemical reaction

precipitation: in *weather*, the conversion of water vapour in the atmosphere into rain, snow, or hail

pressure system: a large area of the atmosphere that possesses a relatively constant pressure, after allowing for differences in height above sea level; *isobars* on weather maps define the area occupied by individual pressure systems

probability: the chance that an event will occur

producer: organisms that convert light (or also thermal) energy into chemical energy that is used by themselves and organisms that consume them in an ecosystem; also, *autotroph*

products: the substances that are produced as the result of a chemical equation-products are found on the right side of a chemical reaction equation

prokaryote: cells that do not possess a membrane-bound nucleus or other membrane-bound organelles; e.g. bacteria

propagate: also *reproduce*, a method of producing more cells or organisms from a single cell or organism

protein: a large molecule that is synthesized on the ribosome according to instructions in DNA; made up of amino acids joined in long chains

proton: a positively charged subatomic particle that is contained within the nucleus and has a mass of 1.67×10^{-27} kg

pure substance: matter that has a set of definite physical and chemical properties whose components are the same and cannot be separated by physical means

radiation: matter and energy that is released by a nuclear reaction or a radioactive element

radioactivity: the spontaneous release of high-energy radiation and particles from the atoms of some elements

radioisotope: an isotope of an element that is radioactive; e.g., Carbon-14

reactant: any substance that is changed as a result of a chemical reaction: reactants are found on the left side of a chemical reaction equation

reaction: a chemical change or transformation; see also *chemical change*

reaction equation: a statement that describes a chemical reaction using the chemical formulas of the reactants and products; see also *chemical equation*

reactivity: the tendency for a substance to take part in a chemical reaction.

relative reactivity: the reactivity of one substance compared with another; for example, since francium will react more readily than argon, francium has a higher relative reactivity than argon

renewable resource: a natural resource, usually an energy source, that can be replaced; e.g., trees

replacement reaction: a chemical change in which one or more ions are exchanged to form products that are neither more complex or simpler than the reactants; see also *single replacement reaction, double replacement reaction*

respiration: see *cellular respiration*

respiratory system: a system in an organism that functions in exchange of oxygen and carbon dioxide gases for the purpose of cellular respiration

responding variable (dependent variable): the variable in an experiment in which a change is detected and that is caused by a change in the manipulated variable

ribosome: a particle in a cell that is composed of subunits and functions in the synthesis of proteins in both prokaryotes and eukaryotes

Second Law of Thermodynamics: states that heat (thermal energy) flows spontaneously transfers from an area of high temperature to an area of low temperature

semipermeable membrane: a membrane such as a biological membrane, through which some, but not all, materials pass

sessile organism: an organism that is incapable of movement independent of other moving bodies

single replacement reaction: a chemical reaction in which one ion is exchanged between one reactant and another

smelting: a process in which metals are extracted from minerals and ores using heat

solar energy: energy in the form of heat and radiation that is emitted from the sun; this energy is used in the photosynthesis reaction

solar energy: energy from the sun in the form of solar radiation; expressed in units of joules (J)

solid: a state of matter in which its molecules cannot move in relation to one another

solubility: the ability or inability of a compound to dissolve in a specific solvent

soluble: capable of being dissolved e.g., if something is soluble in water, it can be dissolved in water

solute: a substance that is dissolved in a solvent

solution: a homogeneous mixture of a solute dissolved in a solvent at a particular concentration

solvent: a substance, usually a liquid, in which a solute is dissolved

sound energy: energy due to the uniform vibration (wave vibration) of molecules

specific heat capacity: a measure of the amount of energy that is required to change the temperature of a specific mass of a substance by one degree celsius (°C)

speed: a measure of a distance moved per unit of time; expressed in units such as m/s or km/h

starch: a storage form of carbohydrate used by plants

state: also *phase*; a physical property of a substance that identifies whether it is a solid, a liquid, or a gas

steady-state system: a system in which the amount of energy that enters the system is equal to the amount of energy that leaves the system

stoma: plural *stomata*, opening in the surface of a leaf that is capable of opening and closing, through which gas exchange occurs and through which water escapes the plant by transpiration

stratus cloud: *stratus* means "spread out"; a cloud that is spread out across the sky

subatomic particles: particles that are contained within the atoms, specifically protons, neutrons, and electrons

substance: matter that has a specific chemical structure and composition surroundings

surface tension: the tendency of the surface of a liquid to contract to the smallest area because of the force of attraction between like molecules; molecules at the surface of a liquid are pulled toward molecules in the interior of the body of liquid, creating a thin surface film of "compressed" liquid that can support objects such as an insect standing on water or the meniscus (rounded shape of the surface) formed in a narrow tube containing liquid

synthesis reaction: see *formation reaction*

synthesize: the formation of a new chemical from its component elements

system (in a biological sense): a group of tissues and organs that function cooperatively to accomplish a specialized task(s)

temperature: a measure of the hotness or coldness of a body with respect to some scale

thermal energy: a form of kinetic energy that is due to the random motion of molecules; energy due to the motion of particles making up an object; also referred to as heat

thermal exhaust (waste energy): the thermal energy that is lost to the environment during an exothermic chemical reaction; the heat energy that is produced and lost as waste during any energy conversion process

total energy: the sum of all energy (of all different types) possessed by an object or system; expressed in units of joules (J)

transition metal: a metallic element that belongs to groups 3–12 on the Periodic Table

transpiration: the process by which plants lose water (mainly from the leaves) by evaporation and by because of which water is pulled up from the roots to the higher parts of the plant

turgor pressure: the outward pressure exerted by the water in a cell on the cell wall; the force that maintains the rigidity of a cell and, in plants, that is responsible for preventing wilting

uniform motion: motion at a constant speed; that is, no acceleration is occurring

vacuum: a volume of space that contains no matter

valence electron: an electron that occupies the highest (outermost) energy level of an atom

valence electron shell: the highest (outermost) energy level in an atom that contains electrons

vaporize: see *evaporate*

vegetative growth: multiplication of cells by mitosis; e.g., during growth of a plant cell

velocity: ratio of change in position to time expressed in units of metres per second

waste energy: the amount of energy lost in an energy conversion; expressed in units of joules (J)

weather: a description of the short-term changes in temperature, precipitation, humidity, air pressure, wind direction and velocity, storms, and cloud cover

weight: a measure of the force of gravity on an object

WHMIS: see *Workplace Hazardous Materials Information System*

work: the transfer of energy; expressed in units of joules (J)

Workplace Hazardous Materials Information System: a standardized system that provides specific information on the properties and negative effects of chemicals found in laboratories, industry, and households

x-intercept: the point at which the plot of a graph crosses the *x*-axis

xylem: dead tubular plant tissue that conducts water and nutrients from the roots to the leaves

y-intercept: the point at which the plot of a graph crosses the *y*-axis

MATERIAL SAFETY DATA SHEET

SECTION 1 - PRODUCT IDENTIFICATION AND USE

PRODUCT IDENTIFIER	SODIUM HYDROXIDE	PRODUCT IDENTIFICATION NUMBER (PIN):	UN-1823

PRODUCT USE Pharmaceutic aid (alkalizing agent)

MANUFACTURERS NAME: N.AV.		SUPPLIERS NAME: XYZ Chemicals	
STREET ADDRESS: N.AV.		STREET ADDRESS: 1234 56 St	
CITY: N.AV.	PROVINCE: N.AV.	CITY: Anywhere	PROVINCE: AB.
POSTAL CODE: N.AV.	EMERGENCY TELEPHONE NO: N.AV.	POSTAL CODE:	EMERGENCY TELEPHONE NO:

SECTION 2 - HAZARDOUS INGREDIENTS

HAZARDOUS INGREDIENTS	%	CAS NUMBER	LD_{50} OF INGREDIENT (SPECIFY SPECIES AND ROUTE)	LD_{50} OF INGREDIENT (SPECIFY SPECIES AND ROUTE)
Sodium hydroxide	98-100	1310-73-2	RAT: ORAL: 104 mg/kg	N.AV.

SECTION 3 - PHYSICAL DATA

PHYSICAL STATE	ODOUR AND APPEARANCE	ODOUR THRESHOLD (ppm)
Solid	Odorless, white hygroscopic crystals	N.AV.

VAPOUR PRESSURE (mmHg) 42@1000	VAPOUR DENSITY (AIR = 1) N.AV.	EVAPORATION RATE N.AV.	BOILING POINT (C) 1390	FREEZING POINT (C) 318
pH 5% aq. Soln. =14	SPECIFIC GRAVITY 2.1	COEFF. WATER/OIL DIST. N.AV.		

SECTION 4 - FIRE AND EXPLOSION DATA

FLAMMABILITY YES ☐ NO ☐   IF YES, UNDER WHAT CONDITIONS?

MEANS OF EXTINCTION Water spray; CO_2; dry chemical

FLASHPOINT (C) AND METHOD N.AV.	UPPER FLAMMABLE LIMIT (% BY VOLUME) N.AV.	LOWER FLAMMABLE LIMIT (% BY VOLUME) N.AV.
AUTOIGNITION TEMPERATURE (C) N.AV.	HAZARDOUS COMBUSTION PRODUCTS May release toxic fumes of sodium oxide which can react with water or steam	

SECTION 5 - REACTIVITY DATA

CHEMICAL STABILITY YES ☐ NO ☐   IF NO, UNDER WHICH CONDITIONS?

INCOMPATIBILITY WITH OTHER SUBSTANCES YES ☐ NO ☐   IF SO, WHICH ONES?   Reacts exothermically with water; acids; aldehydes; unsaturated compounds polymerize violently; aluminum; kalogenated hydrocarbons metals; nitro hydrocarbon to form explosive salts.

REACTIVITY, AND UNDER WHAT CONDITIONS N.AV.

HAZARDOUS DECOMPOSITION PRODUCTS N.AV.

PRODUCT IDENTIFIER	SODIUM HYDROXIDE

SECTION 6 - TOXICOLOGICAL PROPERTIES

ROUTE OF ENTRY

SKIN CONTACT ☐   SKIN ABSORPTION ☐   EYE CONTACT ☐   INHALATION ☐   INGESTION ☐

EFFECTS OF ACUTE EXPOSURE TO PRODUCT   Severe burns to skin, eyes and mucous membranes; possible corneal ulceration and opacification; possible pulmonary edema; ingestion corrosive to respiratory tract.

EFFECTS OF CHRONIC EXPOSURE TO PRODUCT   Possible bronchial pneumonia; severe burns as in acute exposure; ingestion may lead to severe abdominal pain and performation of esophagus and stomach.

EXPOSURE LIMITS	IRRITANCY OF PRODUCT	SENSITIZATION OF PRODUCT	CARCINOGENICITY
N.AV.	Yes (severe to eyes, skin and mucous membranes)	N.AV.	N.AV.

TERATOGENICITY	REPRODUCTIVE TOXICITY	MUTAGENICITY	SYNERGISTIC PRODUCTS
N.AV.	N.AV.	N.AV.	N.AV.

SECTION 7 - PREVENTATIVE MEASURE

PERSONAL PROTECTIVE EQUIPMENT
SEE BELOW

GLOVES (SPECIFY)	RESPIRATOR (SPECIFY)	EYE (SPECIFY)
Yes (rubber)	Mask with dust and mist respirator	Safety goggles, face shield

FOOTWEAR (SPECIFY)	CLOTHING (SPECIFY)	OTHER (SPECIFY)
Yes (rubber)	Coveralls or lab coat	Eyewash equipment nearby

ENGINEERING CONTROLS (SPECIFY eg. VENTILATION,ENCLOSED PROCESS)
Local exhaust

LEAK AND SPILL PROCEDURE
Sweep or shovel up for disposal. If liquifies, take up with sand or other inert absorbent.

WASTE DISPOSAL
According to local, provincial and federal regulations

HANDLING PROCEDURES AND EQUIPMENT
Avoid contact and inhalation

STORAGE REQUIREMENTS
Room temperature in tightly-closed containers

SPECIAL SHIPPING INFORMATION
Corrosive tag

SECTION 8 - FIRST AID MEASURES

SPECIFIC MEASURES

SKIN   WASH WITH WATER FOR 15 MINUTES.

EYES   WASH WELL WITH WATER FOR 15 MINUTES, OCCASIONALLY LIFTING UPPER AND LOWER EYELIDS.

INHALATION   REMOVE TO FRESH AIR. IF NOT BREATHING, GIVE ARTIFICIAL RESPIRATION. KEEP PERSON WARM AT REST.

INGESTION   DO NOT USE GASTRIC LAVAGE OR EMESIS. DILUTE TO ALKALI BY GIVING WATER OR MILK TO DRINK IMMEDIATELY AND ALLOWING VOMITING TO OCCUR. AS SOON AS POSSIBLE, HAVE QUALIFIED MEDICAL PERSONNEL DO ESOPHAGOSCOPY AND IRRIGATE WITH 1% ACETIC ACID TO NEUTRALIZE THE ALKALI.

IF SKIN IRRITATION PERSISTS AND IN ALL OTHER CASES, GET IMMEDIATE MEDICAL ATTENTION.

SECTION 9 - PREPARATION DATE OF M.S.D.S.

PREPARED BY (GROUP, DEPARTMENT, ETC.)	PHONE NUMBER	DATE:
CONTROL DEPARTMENT		

311

ORDERING INFORMATION

SCHOOL ORDERS

Please contact the Learning Resource Centre (LRC) for school discount and order information.

***THE KEY* Study Guides** are specifically designed to assist students in preparing for unit tests, final exams, and provincial examinations.

***THE KEY* Study Guides** – $29.95 each plus G.S.T.

SENIOR HIGH		JUNIOR HIGH	ELEMENTARY
Biology 30	Biology 20	English Language Arts 9	English Language Arts 6
Chemistry 30	Chemistry 20	Math 9	Math 6
English 30-1	English 20-1	Science 9	Science 6
English 30-2	Mathematics 20-1	Social Studies 9	Social Studies 6
Applied Math 30	Physics 20	Math 8	Math 4
Pure Math 30	Social Studies 20-1	Math 7	English Language Arts 3
Physics 30	English 10-1		Math 3
Social Studies 30-1	Math 10 Combined		
Social Studies 30-2	Science 10		
	Social Studies 10-1		

Student Notes and Problems (SNAP) Workbooks contain complete explanations of curriculum concepts, examples, and exercise questions.

SNAP Workbooks – $29.95 each plus G.S.T.

SENIOR HIGH		JUNIOR HIGH	ELEMENTARY
Biology 30	Biology 20	Math 9	Math 6
Chemistry 30	Chemistry 20	Science 9	Math 5
Applied Math 30	Mathematics 20-1	Math 8	Math 4
Pure Math 30	Physics 20	Science 8	Math 3
Math 31	Math 10 Combined	Math 7	
Physics 30	Science 10	Science 7	

Visit our website for a tour of resource content and features or order resources online at
www.castlerockresearch.com

#2340, 10180 – 101 Street
Edmonton, AB Canada T5J 3S4
e-mail: learn@castlerockresearch.com

Phone: 780.448.9619
Toll-free: 1.800.840.6224
Fax: 780.426.3917

ORDER FORM

Learning Resources Centre

Castle Rock Research is pleased to announce an exclusive distribution arrangement with the Learning Resources Centre (LRC). Under this agreement, schools can now place all their orders with LRC for order fulfillment. As well, these resources are eligible for applying the Learning Resource Credit Allocation (LRCA), which gives schools a 25% discount off LRC's selling price. Call LRC for details.

Learning Resources Centre

Orders may be placed with LRC by
Telephone: 780.427.2767
Fax: 780.422.9750
Internet: www.lrc.education.gov.ab.ca
Or mail: 12360 – 142 Street NW
Edmonton, AB T5L 4X9

PAYMENT AND SHIPPING INFORMATION

Name: _____
School Telephone: _____
SHIP TO
School: _____
Address: _____
City: _____ Postal Code: _____
PAYMENT
□ by credit card
VISA/MC Number: _____
Expiry Date: _____
Name on card: _____
□ enclosed cheque   P.O. number: _____
□ invoice school

THE KEY	QUANTITY
Biology 30	
Chemistry 30	
English 30-1	
English 30-2	
Applied Math 30	
Pure Math 30	
Physics 30	
Biology 20	
Chemistry 20	
English 20-1	
Mathematics 20-1	
Physics 20	
Social Studies 20-1	
English 10-1	
Math 10 Combined	
Science 10	
Social Studies 10-1	
English Language Arts 9	
Math 9	
Science 9	
Social Studies 9	
Math 8	
Math 7	
English Language Arts 6	
Math 6	
Science 6	
Social Studies 6	
Math 4	
English Language Arts 3	
Math 3	

Student Notes and Problems Workbooks	QUANTITY	
	SNAP Workbooks	Solution Manuals
Math 31		
Biology 30		
Chemistry 30		
Applied Math 30		
Pure Math 30		
Physics 30		
Biology 20		
Chemistry 20		
Mathematics 20-1		
Physics 20		
Math 10 Combined		
Science 10		
Math 9		
Science 9		
Math 8		
Science 8		
Math 7		
Science 7		
Math 6		
Math 5		
Math 4		
Math 3		

TOTALS
KEYS
SNAP WORKBOOKS
SOLUTION MANUALS
SOLUTION MANUALS

CASTLE ROCK
RESEARCH CORP

#2340, 10180 – 101 Street, Edmonton, AB T5J 3S4   **Phone:** 780.448.9619 **Fax:** 780.426.3917
Toll-free: 1.800.840.6224
Email: learn@castlerockresearch.com
www.castlerockresearch.com